How To Live Without Electricity — And Like It

by Anita Evangelista

Kidron, Ohio

How To Live Without Electricity— And Like It
© 1997 by Anita Evangelista

Published by:
Lehman's
289 Kurzen Road North
Dalton, Ohio 44618

Cover and illustrations by Shary Flenniken

ISBN-13: 978-097887190-1
ISBN-10: 097887190-1
(previously ISBN 0-9666932-1-3)
Library of Congress Card Catalog 98-87562

Contents

Chapter One
Electricity, Power, And All That

In January 1996, during the events which mainstream media have dubbed The Blizzard, the power was out to over half a million homes in North Carolina. And to a million and a half customers in the Northeast. And another couple of million in the upper Midwest. And let's not forget those damp souls in the Northwest, with their floods and power outages.

Most of the residents of those homes were sitting in the dark or with a couple of "emergency" candles burning. Some of those people were also colder than they had been in their lives — heating systems which depend on electricity were as utterly silent as the snow falling outside their darkened windows. And, of course, the freezer was thawing at the same time... but because the stove was electric, or needed an electric spark to trigger its gas pilot light, all those formerly frozen steaks and peas couldn't be cooked and ended up condemned to the trash.

It was the final decade of the twentieth century and these people were living like Stone Age savages, hunkering in their man-made caves without light, without heat, without a microwave, without the technology that has made our century prosperous. In fact, a Stone Age savage probably would be better prepared for the cold and dark because that primitive *wasn't completely dependent* on a fragile gridwork of copper wires.

If the electrical systems worked as the prophets of the 1950s predicted, there would never be an outage and we would all be living lives of modern automated luxury. And at low cost.

But Don't Get Me Wrong...

But don't get me wrong. I enjoy the benefits of electric power — perhaps in a way that other folks cannot appreciate, because my family of four lived without the powerline for three years.

At the beginning of our non-electric adventure, we used no stored power sources whatsoever — we returned to the nineteenth century methods of lighting, heating and cooking. We collected rainwater for drinking and washing, heating it on a wood cookstove and in solar "barrels." We stored our food in underground "cool storage" and "cold boxes" and made our own "ice box." As time went by, we added a portable propane camp stove to our repertoire, and tried out various non-electric lighting systems, including candle-making, oil

---

lamps, propane lamps, and solar-battery lamps. We practiced with solar-energy sources, with solar ovens and wood-fired outdoor stoves, and tried using gas-powered electrical generators. We played with small inverters, converting DC power to AC so we could run the blender, turn on the VCR, or type a letter on the word processor. We tried "animal power" and "human power" generation, and experimented briefly with "wind power." We made mistakes, followed dead-ends, and spent more time than anyone should trying to duplicate the benefits of the powergrid without the expense and dependency.

The most significant discovery we made was also the most humbling one: we were very poorly prepared to live without electricity.

Most people today are equally unprepared — and if the wind rends or sleet tears those fragile copper wires from their moorings, we're stuck back in the Stone Age, but without the caveman's savvy.

What This Book Can Do For You

This book can save you the trouble of learning about power sources from scratch — you won't have to risk spending $500 for a gas-powered generator, because I'll tell you what worked for me and what didn't work at all. When you acquire a kerosene lamp, you'll know which ones give the best and clearest light and which ones will fill your house with fumes. This book will discuss the limits of solar power (which the solar industry conveniently fails to mention), and the remarkable convenience of that very overlooked 12-volt battery you've got sitting near your house right now. We'll look at a whole range of propane- or gasoline-powered appliances that can replace those electric ones.

If you are looking for a means to deal with the inevitable power outages that happen during short-term severe weather or other long-term disruptions, *this book will help you prepare.*

If you're trying to cut down your electric bills by switching to other power sources, *this book will help you find them.*

If you want to convert away from the grid entirely, *this book will help you plan and develop your own multi-source system.*

At the same time, I hope you'll also discover that being off the grid — whether temporary or permanent — can have a very enjoyable side, as well. If you've ever opened a "pit oven," and inhaled the rich, fragrant aroma of a meal cooked by nothing more than hot coals, for free, you *know* that you can live without electricity... and like it.

Know Your Needs

Almost everyone in the civilized world consumes more electric power than they "need." "Need" is the key word of this discussion, by the way — because what we want isn't the same as what we need. On crispy frozen winter mornings, when I step dripping out of the shower I *want* to dry my hair IMMEDIATELY and INSTANTLY, using an electric hair dryer (1200 watts).

But do I really *need* the saving of five minutes that comes from the use of the dryer? Most of the time, I don't. Most of the time, using the dryer is an extravagant convenience. Some of the time, it *seems* like a necessity (such as when I'm running late and just have to wash my hair). But, in reality, that's all baloney — no human being requires a hair dryer in order to function in a rich, full life. Or an electric toothbrush, or electric pencil sharpener, or electric carving knife, or... I'll bet you could name some electric appliance in your own home that's a "want," but not a "need."

And, I'd bet you could also identify some electric things that you believe *are* necessities. Most people put their refrigerator or freezer on the "need" list. The washing machine might also be on that list — and the water pump, if you have a rural residence. We'll discuss alternatives to these "needs" later in this book, but now is a good time to consider what is important and what isn't.

One way to help figure your true electric needs is to compile a list of the power devices you currently use. Take some time and go through this following list, adding your own items to it. You can find the wattage rating on the back of or underneath the appliance where the cord attaches — generally, it is shown as 120V/240 50W — the "50W" shows it uses 50 watts. I'll help you compute your electric usage when you're done.

How To Live Without Electricity
— And Like It

6

Electric Device	Power Usage	x Hours/Day	= Total Use
Air Conditioner	4500 watts		
Battery Charger	30		
Blender	350		
Bread Machine	650		
Clock	30		
Coffee pot	150		
Computer System	400		
Dishwasher	1500		
Dryer	1500-3000		
Fan	50		
Fax	300		
Food Dryer	350		
Freezer	600		
Fry Pan	1500		
Hair Dryer	1200		
Heater, Portable	1500		
Space	2000		
Light, Incandescent	60, 100, 150, 300		
Fluorescent	12-40		
Microwave	600-900		
Night light	10		
Power Drill	900		
Power Saw	1500		
Refrigerator	900		
Stereo	300-500		
Stove, small burner	600		
Large burner	1500		
Oven	4000		
Toaster	1000		
Toaster Oven	1500		
TV - 19" Color	300		
10" B&W	60		
VCR	150		
Washer	600		
Water Heater	4000		
Water pump	2000		
Word Processor	200		

Figuring Your Usage

Grab your pencil and calculator (solar- and battery-powered, of course!) and get prepared for a little painless mathematics. This exercise isn't vital to understanding the rest of the book, but it can be very revealing as to how your power-dollars disappear each month. It can also help you decide which devices you will choose to run during power-short times.

We're going to calculate your actual power use in just a moment, but first, a little electric background.

The thing we call "power" is actually a rather precise measure of the movement of tiny energy packets, electrons. These little electrons flow along copper wires in much the same way that water flows down a steambed. The rate of flow of electrons, the speed at which they move down the wire, is measured in amperes, or "amps" for shorthand. Amps can be thought of as a "current" of electrons, in the same way you think of water having a current.

Just as water encounters rocks and downed tree limbs that impede its progress down river, electrons encounter their own form of resistance. This kind of resistance generally manifests itself as friction from the distance the electrons must travel through the wires, or as changes in air temperature and humidity. And the energy that our electron friends must use to get through this resistance shows up as heat or heat loss along the power lines. The way resistance is referred to by electricians is as units called "ohms".

Now, if you want to find how much strength you'd need to toss a bucket full of water over a boulder blocking your river bed, you'd figure that using the same system electricians use to figure the energy needed to move one amp of current over one ohm of resistance. In fact, that "tossing strength" is called "volts" or "voltage," and represents a specific amount of energy.

Stated in official terms, voltage is equal to current multiplied by the resistance. Hold this thought for a moment.

The electric *power* which we get from the power lines or from batteries is the speed or rate at which electrons are transferred. Power is measured in "watts" units — and every watt is the result of multiplying voltage times amps of current.

Okay. With that background, we can look directly at our power source. Keep in mind that one watt is a pretty small amount of electrical energy — so small that we usually calculate power in thousands of watts: kilowatts. One kilowatt is the same as 1000 watts.

And because a kilowatt can also be used in the blink of an eye, electricity usage is usually measured by the amount of thousands of watts, kilowatts, consumed in an hour. This is called a "kilowatt-hour," or kwh for short. It means, "the number of kilowatts used in precisely one hour."

In an ordinary house, we might easily find ten 100-watt light bulbs. Each of these bulbs consume 100 watts — that is, one-tenth of a kilowatt. If you turn on all these lights simultaneously, you'd be using ten times 100 watts: one kilowatt. If you leave these all on for one hour exactly, you'd have used up one kwh (kilowatt-hour) of power. If you used twice as many light bulbs, twenty of them, and burned them for one hour, you'd use two kwh (that is, 20 x 100 watts x 1 hour = 2000 watts per hour or 2 kilowatt-hours).

Average electricity costs (which you can find on your electric bill or by calling your electric company) vary around the country, from lows of 6¢ per kwh to about 15¢ per kwh. Using an average of 10¢ per kwh for our example, we can figure the cost of keeping one of those 100 watt (1/10th kilowatt) bulbs going for an evening. Let's say you've got the light on for five hours. Here's how to calculate it:

5 hours x 1/10 kilowatt x 10¢ per kwh = 5¢

This is pretty inexpensive. If you were using a single 100 watt bulb every night for a month, you'd hardly spend any money at all on electricity — 5¢ x 30 nights = $1.50 per month. The thing is, it's awfully easy to have five bulbs burning (500 watts), while the TV set is on (300 watts), at the same time the freezer is humming (600 watts) and someone is taking a nice, hot shower using the electric water heater (4000 watts).

Want to see how much that perfectly normal usage would cost per month?

For comparison purposes, let's assume the freezer only runs its cooling motor for six hours daily — its engine cycles on and off depending on the freezer's internal temperature and the outside air temperature. And, let's figure that two folks in your house take a half-hour shower per day, a total of one hour of water heater use. (You can tell we are making this a rough figure — you'd use your water heater for washing dishes, and intermittent hand washing, and it would cycle on and off during the day, too, just to keep the temperature up.) Here are the figures:

Lights:
    5 hours x .5 kilowatt (500 watts, remember) x 10¢ = 25¢
TV:
    5 hours x .3 kilowatt x 10¢ = 15¢
Freezer:
    6 hours x .6 kilowatt x 10¢ = 36¢
Water heater:
    1 hour x 4 kilowatts x 10¢ = 40¢

Total cost: 25¢ + 15 + 36¢ + 40¢ = $1.16 per day.

Monthly cost: 30 days x $1.16 per day = $34.80

Now throw in a couple of shower-addicted teenagers, an electric clothes dryer (3500 watts), a toaster oven (1500 watts), some power tools (4000 watts), and an air conditioner (3000 to 6000 watts). It's no wonder electricity bills are through the roof!

In the same way, you can figure your own typical electrical usage, using the numbers you wrote down in the earlier section. It becomes clear that the higher-usage items in the household are the ones that really drink electricity (that is, eat money) — and, often these are the ones we can live most readily without. For instance, air conditioning is often a luxury rather than a necessity (excluding, possibly, those living in the desert regions and southern Florida, or when health conditions require it). Replacing the icy coldness of the air conditioner with two 50-watt fans will cut your electric usage by at least 40% immediately — and that's a significant savings. Chapter Six has more ideas for cutting your cooling costs.

Why Bother Concerning Yourself With Electricity?

Try this little experiment: go to your house's fuse box or main power source and turn it off on Friday night and turn it back on Sunday night. Spend the weekend without electricity. You'll discover some very interesting things about how you use electricity from the power company, and how dependent you are on the presence of a continuous current. You might find some remarkable things about preparedness, free time, family entertainment, cooking, and personal comfort. It can be quite surprising.

There is a certain type of person who seems to believe that there are no potential complications in our society. This kind of person apparently never gets laid off from work, never experiences fierce weather or power outages, and never has more expenses than he or she has money. For the rest of us, life's up and downs seem to be coming at a more rapid clip.

It seems like every week brings another news report of some extensive region suddenly without electric power. It may be caused by tornadoes, hurricanes, typhoons, bad thunderstorms, ice storms, volcanoes — or from something as simple as a large tree falling on a main power transmission line. In the past, when power was off for a day or so, the suffering was minimal. Sure, the freezer's contents got soggy and you couldn't flip the lights or the TV on. But it seems today that our dependency on the power company makes the inevitable outages much more difficult.

Remember going to the bank and finding out that their "computer lines were down" and they couldn't access your account? If you use credit cards, your ability to purchase necessities may be cut short if the power is off. Power outages to the neighborhood supermarket means a lot more than no lights while you shop — it means the cash registers don't work, along with the refrigerators and freezers that keep our foods safe to eat.

Even solar flares, if they are large enough, can send power surges down lines to ruin circuits, equipment, and house wiring. This kind of solar flare disrupted power for a half-day throughout the Northeast in March, 1992 — and there is no way to predict or prevent solar disruptions to power.

Still stranger, in the Hawaii area, power was off for about 18 hours in 1995, caused by what is believed to have been an "electromagnetic pulse" (EMP) generated by a meteorite that entered the upper atmosphere and detonated. Nobody is absolutely certain if that's what happened. For a short while, American defense systems were on the alert with the concern that a hostile nation had detonated an atomic weapon over the Pacific — an airline pilot even saw what appeared to be a nuclear "mushroom cloud" at the site of the detonation.

Although it's a long shot, just try to imagine the short- and long-term effects if that meteorite had detonated over North America. Aside from the household effects from the EMP (no freezer, no TV, a wrecked VCR, etc.), communication over phone lines might have been interrupted (that's credit card transactions, banking communications, bank computers), records stored on computers of all kinds might have been wiped clean, even emergency communications might have been halted. For a time, we wouldn't even have known what caused the problem, since we couldn't have gotten radio transmissions from facilities that were blacked out.

It might be a long shot to concern ourselves with incoming meteorites and their electrical effects — but you can be absolutely certain that *your power will be off for one reason or another, when you least expect it.* It is inevitable. It is going to happen — and for some readers it may already have happened.

And when it does, you can suffer along with the unprepared crowd... or take some steps so that you are merely inconvenienced or have no discomfort at all. It all depends on what you do next, right now, and in the way you think and plan.

Chapter Two
Let There Be Light!

Lighting is, perhaps, the first and easiest adjustment to make when you part company with the grid. There are not only many types of lighting alternatives, which we'll examine in this chapter, but there are also low-cost alternatives, emergency alternatives, and relatively renewable alternatives.

It's useful to keep in mind the fact that very few lighting systems equal the ease or quality of standard house lights. Even if you decide to go to solar-powered lighting, your usage and lamps will be different. Generally, house lights are used to cast a diffuse light all over the room — with all alternative systems, you'll get used to focusing lights on specific tasks. Your reading light, for instance, will be set next to your comfy chair, not somewhere in the ceiling. If you switch to gas, oil or candles, you'll also become accustomed to a dimmer room lighting (kind of like mood lighting), and carrying your light with you from room to room.

Important Caution

There are three important safety rules which you MUST observe at all time.
1. *Never leave a candle, lamp, or anything with a flame unattended, especially if you have children!!!* If you leave a room, either blow out the flame or take it with you. If you have children, do NOT put candles within their reach; do NOT purchase glass-base lamps — even the best, most disciplined, most careful child can accidentally bump against a table and overturn a glass lamp and cause a deadly fire.
2. *Blow out lamps if you think you might fall asleep.* The light cast by candles and lamps is so pleasant and comfortable that it is easy to forget to put them out. There is a fire hazard with any unattended lamp — and candles can drip wax all over your furniture and floor if left to burn during the night. Plus, it wastes your light-dollars to keep things burning when no one is using them. If you think you'll need light quickly during the night, keep a battery-powered flashlight handy.
3. *Remember that all flames consume air!* If you have an air-tight insulated house, you MUST crack open a window (two would be better) if you are burning any flame in your home. Otherwise, you risk carbon-monoxide asphyxiation — that is, death. If you antici-pate needing light in an airtight space, do not use

flames — get chemical break lights, covered later in the chapter.

Candles

Almost everyone has a few candles in his or her home. They make excellent first-line lighting for both emergencies and long-term mood lights. You can easily read by the light of two candles, do needlework by the light of three, and can keep a medium-sized room moderately lit with six to eight.

Candles come in all shapes, sizes, and costs. Shape and size are largely a matter of personal preference, but costs are often a primary consideration with long-term candle use. If you buy medium-quality candles at department stores (about $2 for two 10" tapers), you will very quickly spend a small fortune to light your house. Five hours of continuous use will burn down an average 10" candle, that is, burn up about a dollar — a good-quality (and more expensive) candle will burn more slowly.

Better-quality candles have a "dense" wax, which is used more slowly than less-expensive candles, and which puts out less soot and smoke. They also cost two to three times what an average candle costs ($3 to $5 each).

How can you keep down your candle costs? The idea of "making your own" might seem an obvious answer here — but it's not. Paraffin for candles is only slightly less expensive than already-made candles. (By the way, paraffin is a by-product of the petroleum industry, a low-grade form of oil — you can safely assume that as gasoline and oil costs go up, so will the cost of paraffin.) Furthermore, dipping candles is time-consuming. Even keeping bees to obtain the fine-quality beeswax for candles becomes a costly way to get wax, since it may cost around $100 to set up a single hive — and then you'd have to wait a year before you could even harvest your first few pounds of wax. (Of course, if you already have bees... that's another story.)

The most efficient way to acquire lots of inexpensive candles is... you guessed it: garage sales and thrift stores. You'll find all shapes, sizes, colors, qualities, and conditions of candles at these low-cost places. In fact, there are so many candles being sold at these outlets that you can easily find unused candles going for 5¢ to 10¢ each. Stock up when you find a bargain price — you'll use all you can get.

Candleholders can be elaborate and beautiful or something as simple as the traditional *paisano* holder of a wine bottle (fill the base with sand so it won't tip over) with a candle stuffed in the top. Candleholders should be made of metal, glass, or ceramic clays — not from unprotected wood, no matter how pretty they are, because wood can catch fire. All candles drip wax (even dripless ones), so a flame-proof plate should be placed beneath all portable holders. Candle sconces, the kind of holders that are permanently attached to the wall, should have either a glass "chimney" around the candle or a protective reflective backing between the candle and the wall. Candles do burn a little longer and with less flickering if they are surrounded by clear glass chimneys.

Remember to save all your candle drippings — these can be recycled into usable candles, too.

Benefits of Candles: Easy to use, inexpensive if you shop around, familiar, the light is tolerable.

Drawbacks of Candles: Wax drips, soot, smoke, fire danger, expensive if bought new.

Costs: 5¢ -10¢ each if bought at thrift shops; about $1 each if new.

Recycled Wax into Light

Save all wax drippings and leftover ends in a heat-proof Mason quart canning jar. When the jar is close to full, place it on a potholder (or several thickness' of towel) in a soup pan filled with cold water up to the level of wax. Be certain that the wax jar won't overturn — lower the water level if necessary. Turn on the heat. The water will eventually boil and gently heat the wax within your Mason jar until it liquefies. Remember that wax can burn, too, so don't let it get too hot.

Use an oven mitt or other protection, and carefully remove the jar of melted wax from the water. Use a fork to stir the wax, and pick out any foreign materials (bits of wick, bugs, etc.). On a heat-proof surface, such as a platter, a cookie pan, or a Pyrex-type baking pan, spray a very light layer of non-stick pan coating (PAM or something similar). Cut a half-dozen 10" to 12" wicks from butcher's string or other cotton string. Now, carefully pour your hot wax onto the surface — it will spread and begin to cool immediately. Keep a close eye on this. As it begins to cool, the wax remains pliable — carefully lay a wick across the wax and begin to lift and roll the wax into a tube with the wick in the center. You may need a dull knife or spatula to scrape the last wax off the surface. If you do this correctly, you will end up with a rather rough but serviceable candle in only a matter of minutes. Lay flat to cool and form your new candle, or place in the refrigerator or outdoors if it's cold out. Trim the wick to about 3/8" on the end you intend to light.

Battery-Powered Lamps

There are all sorts of battery-powered lamps available, some quite reasonable in price and some in the extravagant luxury class of lighting.

Department stores and some catalogs (see Resources) carry these, along with batteries to fit. Very, very few of these items include a statement which declares how long a set of batteries can be expected to last while in continuous use — probably because the use-time is so short. However, some do include info: Coleman's mushroom-shaped "krypton lantern" runs up to 23 hours on four D-cells.

This translates to a high cost for batteries. If the krypton lantern is used five hours for four nights, it'll be time to replace those D batteries — this breaks down to about a dollar per night, just to have one light. Clearly, the cost of using batteries demands a further adjustment... rechargeables. We'll look at rechargeable types of batteries in Chapter Nine. For now, keep in mind that while rechargeables are about twice as expensive to purchase initially as one-use batteries, they really can last for years. Their durability makes them much less expensive in the long run.

The "krypton" light used in the aforementioned lamp is only one type of bulb available. While you can run a standard household light bulb on a battery, you'll get a longer running time (and probably a cleaner light) from fluorescent bulbs. Tall "camp lights" with miniature fluorescent bulbs cast a wide, white light that is fairly good for open spaces, but not to good for close-up reading or handiwork — it's uncomfortable and has dark shadows. However, the light is quite steady, which is a benefit if you're trying to concentrate on something.

These lamps are not inexpensive. Although you can find the Coleman version for around $15, sharp movements tend to upset the bulb and distort the light. Fluorescent lamps run from $60 to $120 each (less expensive ones can be found but are generally inferior).

Benefits of Battery Lamps: Wide-space lighting, clean, easy to replace batteries and bulbs, easy to use.

Drawbacks of Battery Lamps: Startup costs, replacement batteries, bulky shapes.

Costs: Lamps run $15 to $120; batteries to $4 if single-use; rechargeables plus recharger $30.

Oil and Kerosene

For long-term use, oil and kerosene lamps are the ones most often chosen. In part this comes from the ready availability of these lamps, the "familiarity" we have with them from watching TV and movies, and their decent light production. There is a wide variability in the quality of these lamps, though, and in the production of fumes and soot. The top of the line, in both lighting and clean burning, is Aladdin lamps, but they are also one of the most expensive.

Oil Lamps: These are simply an updating of the most ancient lighting system known, where cooking oil — olive oil, soybean, vegetable, etc. — is used as the combustion source. A wick is suspended in the oil, and the tip is lighted. The burning flame draws oil up the wick and burns it to produce light.

Although there are fancy versions of this kind of lamp, they generally are not superior light producers. Lehman's (see Resources) carries an "element" for an olive-oil burner for about $8 — you provide the oil and the Mason jar to hold it. Olive oil is expensive (about $30 per gallon), so other cooking oils should be considered. If overturned, these lamps snuff themselves out, although they will leave a large greasy stain. The light is equivalent to a single candle.

Kerosene Lamps: These are sometimes called "oil" lamps too, dating from the time when people remembered that paraffin, kerosene, and motor oil all came from the same petroleum wells. These burn either "ultra pure oil" (paraffin) or kerosene. The kerosene can come in pretty colored types with various "scents" or in natural form which is fairly clear and quite smelly. All these lamps can be divided into three basic categories: basic, Aladdin, and pump.

Old-style kerosene chamber lamp.
Courtesy of Lehman's, Kidron, Ohio. (330) 857-5757.

"Basic" kerosene lamps run the gamut of prices and qualities, with some less-expensive models running under $10 and better ones for around $50. The least-expensive ones can be found in any department store. They feature a glass chimney, glass kerosene well, and brass or brass-colored burner. A wide flat cotton wick draws the kerosene above the burner, where a flame consumes the liquid and produces light. Some of these lamps are quite attractive, especially when loaded with a colored kerosene. But their ability to provide light is limited by their poor tooling — wicks can slip, chimneys admit too much air, and in general they are difficult to read or do close work by because the flames flicker. They also combust the kerosene incompletely and produce prodigious quantities of chemical-smelling fumes and wall-blackening soot. Higher-priced basic lamps burn somewhat better and cleaner, as do "round-wick" versions. All these lamps also produce heat, so be careful about what you place them near and under. "Aladdin" lamps are the Cadillac of kerosene burners, and with good reason. They come in dozens of styles, have attractive shades, and replacement parts can be readily found. Prices are on the high end, running from about $50 to almost $200, mostly depending on the decoration or beauty of the lamp.

All Aladdins burn kerosene or paraffin oil through a wick-based "mantle" system. The kerosene is drawn by a wick to the spiker-web-like mantle. The mantle distributes the combustible fluid and burns it over the entire mantle area — which produces a bright, clear, unwavering light. A typical Aladdin provides about the same light as a 60-watt bulb. It is easy to read by, do hand work by, and lights rooms quite efficiently. Typically, they burn about 4¢ of fuel per hour per lamp. There is hardly any residual odor and almost no soot buildup.

I've found Aladdins something of a trick to light. The glass chimney must be disengaged by twisting it off, then twisted back on after the mantle is lit — and the chimney is already getting quite hot by the time I've fumbled through this routine. The chimneys feel fragile, though mine have put up with a lot of abuse. And these lamps get *very* hot in use — too hot to leave your hand over the chimney, and plenty hot enough to char a piece of paper placed atop the chimney. Give them lots of space. Hanging Aladdins should be AT LEAST 18" from the ceiling.

A variety of Aladdin kerosene-lamp styles.
Courtesy of Lehman's, Kidron, OH. (330) 857-5757.

While the glass-base and glass-shade Aladdins are probably the most attractive lamps around, like all glass objects they are breakable. Fortunately, Aladdins do have metal bases and paper or cloth shades; there are also wall-mountable lamps such as the "Watchman" style ($90) that see a lot of use overseas where electric lamps are unavailable.

One suggestion that will save you a lot of grief over the years is to get an Aladdin with a kerosene filler plug on the base — otherwise, you'll have to remove the chimney, mantle, and wick each time you want to add fuel.

"Pump"-style lamps, which Lehman's calls "Amish Table Lamps," do appear to operate like the old-style pump lamps. Generally, pump lamps are mantle-types, with an oil reservoir like typical kerosene lamps. By using a hand-held air pump, pressured air is added to the lamp through a valve, and the mantle is lit. The light is excellent, but it must be used with a shade which diffuses the light somewhat. Prices run about $200 for lamp, shade, and pump — though one pump ($18) can be used with many lamps. Lehman's gives a gentle caution about these lamps: "As with any pressure light, read and follow owner's manual and use with caution. Fuel is volatile." I've never heard of any pressure lamp rupturing from over-pressurization, but it is sensible to be aware of the possibility. Pump lamps are clean-burning and heat-producing.

Benefits of Oil/Kerosene Lamps: Familiarity, fairly easy to use, good light in more expensive models, ready accessibility of oil and kerosene.

Drawbacks of Oil/Kerosene Lamps: Fumes and soot in cheaper models, high heat production in more expensive models; high cost of better types; danger of overturning and fires.

Costs: Cheapest — $10; Expensive — $200; Good-quality Aladdins for $90. Kerosene runs about $2 per gallon or so, more expensive at department stores. Paraffin and "ultra oils" may run to $6 a gallon. Replacement parts for better lamps average $14 for chimneys (get several to have on hand for immediate replacement), $5 for wicks, and $5 for mantles.

Amish pump-style kerosene table lamp.
Courtesy of Lehman's, Kidron, OH. (330) 857-5757.

Lanterns and Flashlights

Outdoor lighting, for use in inclement weather or for those nightly trips to the backhouse or barn, has to be sturdier than indoor lighting. Lanterns are generally manufactured with durability and weather-tightness in mind — if they are *real* lanterns. There are many cheap, low-grade knock-offs on the market that are copies of the real things, so carefully inspect and consider before you buy. Fakes are nothing but aggravation; don't fall for any inexpensive lanterns... good ones cost, but they are worth it. Mantle lanterns give off phenomenal amounts of light, around the equivalent of a 200-300-watt bulb. They are fairly economical to operate on kerosene. Some brands, such as Coleman, have "dual fuel" lanterns, which can run on either butane or unleaded gasoline — very handy if you run out of one or the other.

Coleman #639 kerosene lamp.
Courtesy of Lehman's, Kidron, OH. (330) 857-5757.

Coleman's #639, a single-mantle model, holds 32 ounces of fuel, roughly a quart, and burns for 5½ hours on that filling. If you use a generic kerosene, your cost for operation is about 50¢ per filling or less. Dietz lanterns used to be the quality standard, and you can still occasionally find old ones in good condition at garage sales. The new ones I've seen in department stores have not been of the old quality — but these were the bottom-of-the-line ones anyway. I'd avoid any that cost less than $10.

Even though they provide efficient lighting, you shouldn't use lanterns indoors. As a group, they are very smelly and productive of carbon monoxide. If you are going into a barn or dry field, I would not take a flame-lit lantern under any circumstances — the danger of fire is simply too great. This is the proper place for a flashlight.

Flashlights of all types, from the $1 cheapie to $30 jobs are available everywhere. We've found the 4 AA-powered "head lamp" style flashlight ($10) incredibly useful — it leaves both hands free and gives a clear light wherever you look.

The big cost for all flashlights is the batteries, an expense which can be mitigated somewhat by use of rechargeable batteries. Some moderately-priced flashlights are self-contained rechargeables, but my experience with several of these brands has been disappointing — they don't last.

Also disappointing was the "squeeze" flashlight ($10), which runs on an internal flywheel generator operated by squeezing a lever on the handle. This uses no batteries or other power source except for the energy generated by your fist. What a superb idea! Unfortunately, the internal components are plastic and repeated use pretty much destroys the workings —

we've had four and none have lasted more than three weeks of nightly use. For occasional use, these might be a worthwhile product.

Benefits of Lanterns & Flashlights: Good light, very portable, endures harsh weather and temperature extremes.

Drawbacks of Lanterns & Flashlights: Lanterns produce odors and toxic fumes; flashlights are expensive to run because of battery replacement; both will be ruined if dropped once or twice.

Costs: Quality lanterns start at $30; flashlights $1 plus.

Propane Lamps

Here is a very viable but much underused option for a non-electric home lighting system. It is moderately expensive to install if you wish to redo your entire house, fairly inexpensive if you wish to install only one or two lights, and about as potentially hazardous as a propane cooking stove — which is to say, they're pretty safe. The light produced is clear, unwavering, and comparable to a standard 60-watt bulb. Each lamp uses about .083 pounds of propane per hour (about 2/100ths of a gallon), so they are economical to burn.

Lehman's offers two manufacturers' brands of gas lights, both very attractive and stylish. To light, you insert a match beneath the glass globe and flip on the gas. A mantle disperses and burns the gas efficiently.

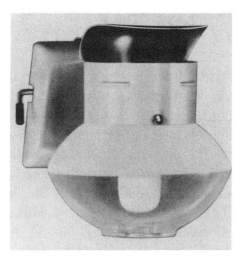

Humphrey Opalite gas light.
Courtesy of Lehman's, Kidron, OH. (330) 857-5757.

Hindmarch Valor gas light.
Courtesy of Lehman's, Kidron, OH. (330) 857-5757.

To install these lights, you need to put in 3/8" copper tubing to carry the propane to your lights. A standard tank-mounted gas regulator set at 11" of water column (a pressure indicator) controls the flow of propane to the mantle. Individual lamps have a manually operated switch, which you turn as you light it; each lamp must be separately lit.

If you live in earthquake-prone areas, you will need a gas shutoff at the propane tank. Copper tubing can be bent or torn during a tremblor, so these lamps should not be used after a shaker until the lines can be professionally or thoroughly checked. This is simplest if the tubing is installed where it is visible. Any time you are able to smell the odor of free propane, do not turn on any flames! Propane leakage is one of the quickest ways to set off an explosion, so treat it with appropriate caution.

Gas lamps are flexible enough, in terms of installation, that you can set up two or three attached to a single-source 20-gallon portable propane tank, the kind of tank used for barbecue grills. When the propane level is low, you simply disengage the tank and have it refilled in town.

Typically, an individual propane light will run about $50. However, you'd also need replacement mantles ($5), a propane source, regulator ($15), and copper tubing ($1 per foot). If you were putting in a single propane lamp three feet from a 20-gallon holding tank and buying all parts new, you'd spend around $100 for the entire set up.

Benefits of Gas Lamps: Easy to use, very economical fuel consumption, relatively safe, excellent steady light.

Drawbacks of Gas Lamps: Moderately expensive to install, possibility of explosion associated with gas use.

Costs: Lamp only, $50. Installation of single lamp and source, about $100.

Solar-Powered Lamps

In essence, lamps which obtain their power from the sun are actually "battery-powered" devices — you use these lamps after the sun has gone down, not while it is still charging them. Solar lamps are often fluorescent, as well, since the bulbs use significantly less energy than incandescent types.

Solar lamps vary in size and style, but many are rather large and bulky. On one side, the solar "cells" are exposed to direct or indirect sunlight for a full day (5 to 12 hours). The cells convert light energy into chemical energy and store the energy in an internal array of rechargeable batteries. In the evening, when you turn the lamp on, that stored energy is used to light the bulbs. A typical solar lamp may run for four to six hours on a charge — although it is more likely that it will light well for about half the expected time, then begin to decline in lighting output for the other half.

These are as easy to use as any battery lamp. They are, however, dependent on sunny weather and on having a responsible person who will set them in the sun. Most of these lamps will be ruined if they are rained upon — so the responsible person must be able to remember to move the lamps indoors in inclement weather. A sunny south-facing window would be a big plus in the charging of solar lamps. (Of course, if you happen to live in the Southern Hemisphere, that would be a north-facing window.) Lamps *will* charge during overcast cold weather, but they charge more slowly and consequently have a smaller charge that lights for a shorter period of time. On short, dark winter days — when the need for a long-burning light is greatest — a solar lamp many need two or three days of charging to accomplish a full charge. Having two or three of these lamps and alternating their use to allow for full charging might be one way to overcome this liability.

Typical lamps cost between $60 and $120 each. This includes the internal batteries.

Benefits of Solar-powered Lamps: After purchase, operation is virtually free; light is fair to good, especially for space lighting; convenient, easy to use.

Drawbacks of Solar-powered Lamps: Moderate to expensive to purchase, require daily placement and attention, bulky, lighting time is variable and possibly shorter than expected.

Costs: $60 to $120 for purchase. Bulbs run less than $5 each and rarely need replacement.

Chemical Lights

These small, portable, lights are most comparable to the quality of light given off by "night lights" — just sufficient to scare off the gremlins of the dark, but not really a comfortable light to read or work by.

Chemical lights are often sold as "break lights" because of the method of "turning on" the light. Each consists of a plastic tube which contains a series of chemicals. When the tube is bent or twisted (the "break" part of the name), it causes the internal chemicals to mix — and that mixture produces a cool phosphorescent light. Tubes stay lit for 4 to 6 hours, cannot be turned off, and cannot be reused. Light, very portable, and easy to use.

A real benefit of chem lights is that they can be used in air-tight spaces or where gas leaks might exist — they neither burn air nor use sparks or flames. They're also ideal companions for children who move around at night but are too young to use candles or operate flashlights. For this reason, chem lights are heavily marketed around Halloween for kids to use during trick-or-treat escapades. The rest of the year, it's harder to find these items — "army/navy surplus" or "survival" stores generally carry one brand or another of these all year.

Benefits of Chemical Lights: Very easy to use, portable, useable in air-tight or gas-leak conditions.

Drawbacks of Chemical Lights: Dim lights, single use.

Costs: Typically, a single light runs 50¢ to $2, depending on size.

Combination Set-Ups

The most flexible system is often the most varied one — too often, when you are dependent on a single type of lighting, something happens to interfere with its operation. A home that has several dozen candles, four or five kerosene lamps, two or three battery and solar lamps, a single gas lamp and a handful of break lights can deal with any kind of lighting situation imaginable. Such a residence can also switch light sources to accommodate different weather conditions (put the solar chargers out on good days, use candles until the solar lamps are recharged, etc.).

For comfort's sake, keep an easily lit lamp, chem light, or flashlight near the bed, no matter what kind of lighting system you decide upon.

And, one more thing — if you use flame-lit lamps, remember to stock up on *matches!*

Chapter Three
Water: How To Get It;
How To Store It

We really take quality water for granted. As a culture, we have simply forgotten that water in other countries (and even in previous centuries in our own country) was a prime source for the spread of numerous deadly diseases — cholera, typhoid fever, typhus, and gastro-enteric bacteria of all types. Today, cryptosporidia and giardia lace public water supplies (remember the Milwaukee outbreak a few years back, with 400,000 people affected?). There's also concern in certain areas about the leaching of agricultural chemicals and sprays into drinking water supplies.

Even so, it is possible to provide a clean, tasty supply of water at home with only a few reasonable precautions and some planning. Basically, there are only two places that water comes from: the sky or the ground. And the real consideration once you have water, is how to store it as a clean supply free of bacteria, industrial contaminants, and crud.

From the Sky

From about 100 degrees longitude (about the middle part of the country) eastward, there is sufficient annual rainfall to more than provide adequate water year around. West of 100 degrees, water is more sporadic, but it is available IF the water is saved and collected in holding tanks. An average house roof over a 25' x 30' structure has over 750 square feet of surface exposed to rain. During a 1" rainfall, a fairly light rain, this roof could provide over 60 gallons of quality water if appropriate measures have been taken to collect that rainfall.

"Appropriate measures" by the way, have been known for literally thousands of years, and are still in use in the Middle East where rainfall is scarce. In this country, you can find the evidence of old cisterns, water-holding tanks, around abandoned farmsteads throughout the Midwestern states. After all, in the pre-deep-well era (that is, before the mid-20th century), the only way to save water was in a cistern.

In essence, what is required to collect rainwater and snow melt are the following: a clean roof or other large flat surface, a means of channeling the water, and a holding area. We'll look at each of these items individually:

Clean Roof: The key word is "clean." Any roof will do, as long as bits and pieces don't routinely get washed down into your collection. All roofs are also exposed to dust, dirt, bugs, leaves, bird droppings and so forth, so a means is needed to channel the first few minutes of rain in each storm AWAY from your holding facility — simply rinse off the roof to provide the cleanest water possible.

Channeling the Water: Diverting that rinse water can be a small part of the tail end of your general collecting system. Typical suburban houses already have a nearly complete collecting system already in place, perhaps without realizing it — it's those old storm gutters on the edge of the roof that channel rain away from the drip line. If these are already in place on your houses and barns, then you simply need to acquire a few extra pieces to connect the gutters so they feed into one holding tank. Or into several holding tanks, if you prefer. Gutters come in galvanized and plastic versions; an average house may require several hundred dollars-worth to completely redo the place.

Diverting the rinse water takes place just before the holding tank. This can be done with something as simple as a section of plastic screen which will catch pieces of junk — or with a slightly more complex arrangement that can be diverted by hand. Hand-diversion requires that someone go out after the first few minutes of a rain, and turn your water spout into the holding tank; the first rain is washing onto the ground and your collected water stays clean. Some enterprising souls have developed a weighted bucket system so that the first rinse water is channeled into a bucket on a see-saw balance. As the bucket fills, it presses on the balance, and the other end rises and turns

---

the water diverter into the holding tank — the simplest kind of "machine," completely gravity-operated!

Holding Tanks: In the old days, cisterns were built into the ground. Shapes varied slightly, but most were something like a bottle or tube form, eight to ten feet deep and three feet across. These were dug by hand, bricked and mortared (the shape allowed the bricks to press in on each other and provided a fairly watertight container). Underground, the water remained cool (which suppressed bacterial growth), and could be either pumped up using a hand-pump or pulled out by a bucket on a rope.

Underground water storage in a cistern. Note the overflow pipe on left and intake pipe at top right.
Illustration by Shary Flenniken.

This system still works just fine. Old cisterns can often be rehabilitated by replastering the interior with a mortar made especially for cisterns. Here in the Ozarks, home cisterns are in common use, although many people no longer collect free rainwater — they prefer to purchase trucked-in city water, which is then stored in their cisterns. Go figure.

Additionally, clean used milk tanks made of stainless steel and large plastic water tanks can be purchased from dairies and farm-supply stores for roughly $1 per gallon of holding capacity. Buried underground beneath the frost line they provide secure, cool water storage throughout the year.

But there is no reason whatsoever to ignore ANY kind of holding tank... we've used plastic trash barrels, the 33-gallon kind, and they are durable, portable collectors. I've seen 600-gallon galvanized livestock-watering troughs pressed into service as holding tanks, former swimming pools doing drinking water duty, and even dug pits lined with plastic tarps acting as water reserves.

One type of holding facility that has gained some popularity in recent years is a ferro-concrete tank. These can be constructed at home by energetic but otherwise inexperienced personnel for minimal cost. Here's how: 100 feet of 48" chicken wire is formed into a tank-sized ring, say 7½ feet in diameter. Each loop of the ring is about 24 feet long (formula is 2 x 3.14 x ½ the diameter of the tank-to-be), so 100 feet of wire will provide four loops. A rough footer area should be dug and finished with concrete, brick, or whatever you have — then a slab or floor is poured over the footer. Put in your outlet pipes at this point, slightly above the floor surface. Using plywood or leftover lumber, make a circular four-foot-high form around the footer, line this with a layer of plastic sheeting, put the chicken wire form around this, and "plaster" the wire heavily with about 66 cubic feet of cement. When dry, remove the form and plastic, and it's ready to go. Above-ground water keeps better if its covered.

Complete and exacting plans by Don R. Wilson, writing in the July/August 1990 *Backwoods Home Magazine* (see Resources), indicate this finished tank will hold about 1100 gallons of water.

Drawing water off of your holding tanks can be accomplished using a small hand pump ($50), a battery-operated pump ($50), a rope-lowered bucket, or by installing outlet piping on an above-ground structure so that gravity does the pumping for you. Water, even if it is as clean as you can make it, may still need filtering, distilling, and/or chlorination, which are covered later in the chapter.

From the Ground

Flowing streams, springs, dug wells, and drilled wells are the four prime sources for water from the ground. Streams, springs, and dug wells are, perhaps, the most convenient water sources — and potentially the easiest to contaminate because of their proximity to the ground surface. Drilled wells are a modern development, and almost all require some kind of pump system to draw up the water — this can be mechanical (hand-operated pump), electrical and battery-driven, or solar powered. Drilled wells, if they are hundreds or thousands of feet deep, are much less likely to be contaminated, but a shallow drilled well can be.

Streams, Springs, Dug Wells: Water can be retrieved using plastic buckets, the simplest and least-expensive gathering system. Streams and springs deliver cleaner water when they are clear and when the water is drawn from moving water some feet away from the bank. If your river flows consistently and doesn't flood very often, you can rig up a plastic pipe so that it collects water and pushes it to a spot on the bank where it is convenient to fill your buckets. At its simplest, this could be a length of straight pipe, suspended with its leading edge under the surface of the water above a fall — the water will flow down the pipe if the end is slightly lower than the leading edge, directly into your bucket.

"Ram" Pumps: If your river flows at a slightly different elevation than your potential-use outlet, you may bene-fit by use of a "ram pump" — a clever device that uses the weight and force of water flowing downhill to send it in pipes uphill. Ram pumps were developed in the late 1700s, and typically require at least two feet of "fall" or drop in water level on the intake side (more is better). They can pump water uphill as much as several hundred feet. Ram pumps can also be connected in series, with some loss of pumping capacity. Flow generally amounts to one gallon per minute, and can be stored in holding tanks until use. Rams use the stored

power in the movement of the water itself, and don't
require any other power supplies. Maintenance is minimal and a ram can last for decades.

Plastic rams, with a potential life of only 3-5 years, can
be found for around $100. Better-quality ones run about
$300 to $500; piping and holding tanks are extra.

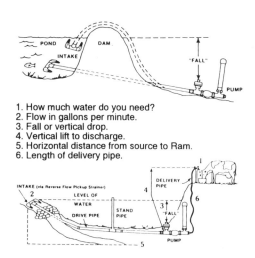

1. How much water do you need?
2. Flow in gallons per minute.
3. Fall or vertical drop.
4. Vertical lift to discharge.
5. Horizontal distance from source to Ram.
6. Length of delivery pipe.

Hydraulic ram pump system.
Courtesy of Kansas Wind Power, Holton, KS. (913) 364-4407.

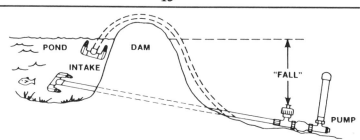

Note that the "fall" of water from the source to the pump has little to do with the LENGTH of the pipe used to feed the pump. For example, with a rapidly falling stream...or from a dam...it may be possible to get a good "fall" from the source to the pump with only a minimal pipe run. But in every case there must be a length of hard ridged pipe so as to create a hammering effect.

HYDRO-RAM HOUSEHOLD WATER SYSTEM

This illustration shows a schematic of a typical gravity-feed water system. The **FLEMING HYDRO-RAM** pumps water to a tank placed higher than the showers, sinks, etc. in the house (an insulated tank in the attic is ideal). Overflow water is either returned to the stream or used for other purposes (such as filling a livestock watering trough). Since the water is constantly being pumped into the tank, the water stays fresh and the chances of it freezing in winter are reduced.

Be sure to check your local plumbing codes before installing any system for household water. **The Ram Co.** can supply all system components.

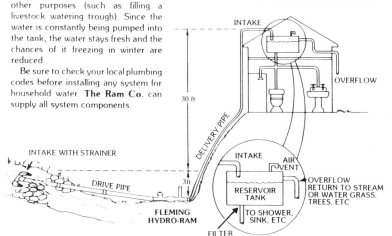

Hydraulic ram pumps use the kinetic energy of water running through a drive pipe to lift a small proportion of that water to a higher level than the supply source. They can operate reliably where there is a steady and continuous supply of water with a fall of 0.8 meters or more. Ram pumps have considerable potential to lift water for small community supplies from unpolluted streams or springs in hilly or mountainous areas.

Fleming Hydro-Ram household water system.
Courtesy of Lehman's, Kidron, OH. (330) 857-5757.

Rife hydraulic rams: "Lehman's Best."
Courtesy of Lehman's, Kidron, OH. (330) 857-5757.

"Kant Freeze" pitcher pump.
Courtesy of Lehman's, Kidron, OH. (330) 857-5757.

Kitchen Pumps: Small "kitchen pumps" or "pitcher pumps" are used to retrieve water from shallow wells or cisterns less than 20 feet deep. Kitchen pumps are small, easy to use, and cost around $60, excluding pipes. Fancy models run up to $250. Intake pipes are placed into your water supply, and by driving a handle up and down, the pump creates a vacuum that sucks water into your pipes. The pump then disgorges the water into your sink or bucket. Maintenance is minimal, and they last for years.

Other Dug-Well Systems: For drops of 40 feet or less, a special chain-driven, scoop-retrieval system can be made for around $250 (excluding the cost of the well itself). These systems can occasionally be found in old Victorian-era homes; Lehman's carries the makings. These operate by means of a crank that drives the chain and drops the scoops into the water. These are drawn up to empty into your portable bucket — up to 15 gallons per minute.

Lehman's also has the means for making a "driven" well — which consists of a series of standard steel water pipes coupled together and a "drive cap." Basically, this is a long shaft, which is banged into the ground. This is pounded into (hopefully) water-rich soil, up to around 20 feet deep. The real benefit of this system is that it doesn't require much in the way of heavy machinery — just a good, strong set of arms and a sledge hammer. Water must be pumped out using a kitchen pump or hand pump.

Drilled Wells: Generally, drilled wells are deeper than dug wells, and may go hundreds to thousands of feet deep. They are "cased," or have steel or plastic pipes that go down the well shaft; most average two inches in width, but some casings are 5" wide ID ("inside diameter" of the pipe).

Drilled wells up to 175 feet deep can be used with a hand-operated pump — go deeper than that and the water is too heavy to draw up by hand. Deep drilled wells may require either a motorized pump (which could be solar), or one driven by windmill power, or even a generator-powered pump.

Hand Pumps: Styles, prices, and qualities vary greatly, but if you plan to use one of these big numbers, keep your strength and needs in mind as you plan.

These pumps require the visible "pump head," a well casing, a drop pipe, a pump rod, and a cylinder. The cylinder is the part that actually contacts the water and contains the valves that provide lift for the water.

If you have a drilled well already, the five components will run between $600 and $1000 to install — but if a well must be drilled, you will spend somewhere in the range of $4000 to infinity for the entire system. Drilling a well can be a very expensive proposition... it's no wonder people still use cisterns.

Hand-pumped, deep-well water can also be stored in holding tanks so that your pump chores are confined to limited times of the day. Some enterprising types have hooked hand pumps up to their home-water supply by pumping into a gravity-fed holding tank that supplies in-house pipes.

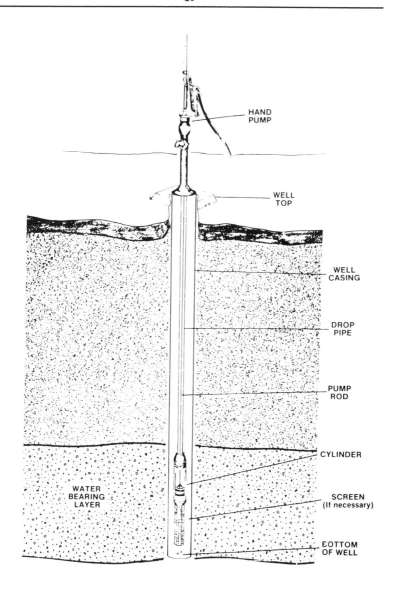

Typical hand pump installation.
Courtesy of Lehman's, Kidron, OH. (330) 857-5757.

Solar and Windmill Pumps: First, plan to spend some real money — either type of system will set you back $2000 and up, depending on how deep your existing well is and how fast you need water to flow.

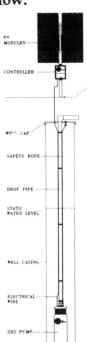

Solarjack SDS solar water pump system.
Courtesy of Kansas Wind Power, Holton, KS. (913) 364-4407.

The ideal of "solar"-powered water pumping has specific applications where wind is inconsistent or too powerful, and where there is lots of year-round sunlight. As with a hand-pump, there's more to it than just a pump — you need a drilled well, a pump, well casing, a solar array (panels to absorb the sunlight and convert it to energy), supports for the array, a holding tank, and a battery backup system for sunless days. Solar pumping is continuous as long as the sun shines, but may only bring up 2 to 5 gallons per hour, depending on the size of the pump. If you are buying everything new, but already have the drilled well, you can spend $6000. If you need to drill a well, too, you'll spend about $10,000.

Solar systems can be damaged by very high winds (that pick up and remove the equipment), and by hail which shatters the panels. In addition, some varieties of panels may need a "tracking" system that follows the sun across the sky for maximum output. Barring mechanical weather damage, a solar system can work quite efficiently for 10 years or more.

"Wind"-powered water pumping is possible wherever there are fairly continuous strong breezes — at least 5 miles per hour, and 15 mph is better. The pump itself, along with cylinder, drop pipe, and pump rod, are of the same variety used with hand pumps, but windpowers can draw water up from much deeper levels. In addition to the regular pump equipment, you will need a stand or tower to support the blades, "propeller" blades for the wind-power head, and a drive shaft to carry the power down to the pump head. If buying new, plan to spend at least $4000 for the entire setup (not including the drilled well). You may be able to find unwanted windmills around old farm sites at low cost and refurbish them for your own use.

Windmills can be damaged by high winds, lightning, and earthquakes. Most modern setups include a "wind-tracking joint" that allows the head to swivel so that it always faces into the wind and can draw the maximum power. Make sure the joint is properly lubricated. Heads can be bothersome to service, since they are so high off the ground — include some kind of ladder system for your own convenience if you are constructing one of these from scratch.

Aside from the cost of occasionally replacing worn parts, windmills can keep working for you for decades.

Pumps and Generators

In an emergency situation, you can plug an electric pump into a portable generator (gasoline or diesel) and bring up water from a drilled well for an hour or two into a holding tank.

Generators are an entire topic in Chapter Nine, but for use as a water-pump power source you will need to know two things: how much "juice" (energy) does your pump draw — and especially what is the "surge" (start up) wattage? You can generally find this information on the pump housing or by contacting the installer. Lacking that, informed well drillers in your area may know what a typical installation uses. The second thing you must know is the maximum output and surge capacity of your generator. This should be indicated by a label somewhere on the generator.

The generator's output must be higher than your pump draws, or it simply won't work — and the generator may burn itself out trying to meet the demand.

Generators are expensive to run and require careful maintenance. If you decide to go this route, don't use a generator to pump up small quantities of water — bring up a full day's supply at one time (about 50 gallons per person in an ordinary household application) or more.

In general, diesel generators have higher capacity ratings, and require less maintenance. Inexpensive department-store generators which cost less than $500 are often not worth the trouble. Be sure to get an automatic "low-oil shut-off" on your gasoline-powered generator, so it won't destroy its engine if oil gets low.

Filters, Purifiers, Distillers

No matter how clean the water appears, I can guarantee you that there is some kind of potentially harmful bacteria lurking in it — one to which you may have become resistant by virtue of daily exposure, but one which may infest infrequent guests and younger relatives with extreme gastric discomfort.

Think about it: that crystal-clear mountain stream contains fish, frogs, insects — all relieving themselves numerous times daily into your drinking water. Deer walk through pristine meadows, stepping into the manure of other animals, and then place their front feet daintily into your pristine stream when they take a drink. Eagles and cranes, flying overhead, drop partially eaten corpses of small creatures into the water (and relieve themselves, as well), and the decomposing rotting bodies of dead fish, birds, bugs, you name it, drift downriver from their original sources. Yes, primitive man drank the same water. Yes, primitive man died of typhoid fever. Yes, modern man has hospitals and antibiotics to relieve his water-caused diarrhea. It is simpler and wiser to assume that your water is contaminated and take steps to purify it, than to assume it is pure and then suffer the consequences.

Bacteria: These are fairly simple to destroy using familiar means — boil the water for 20 minutes. You can also add 15 drops of chlorine per gallon of water, or ¼ cup of hydrogen peroxide per gallon. Thermal or chemical means of purification are very reliable against bacteria — but won't do a bit of good against heavy metals, agricultural chemicals, or off-flavors.

"Casing" your well by covering the surface area around the well outlet is one of the easiest ways to protect wells from bacterial contamination. Deep wells that have this kind of protection are often low in potentially harmful bacteria — that is, until the water has been drawn up and exposed to surface air, containers, and holding tanks.

Fungi, Molds, and Mildews can attack water supplies that are exposed to sunlight, which is why water keeps better when it is covered. That much-maligned chemical agent, sodium hypochlorite — common household bleach — at the rate of 15 drops per gallon of water, will suppress the growth of these slimy nasties. Chlorine bleach, by the way, is the one chemical agent that has safely protected our nation from cholera and typhoid fever during this century. There may be some health risks associated with long-term use of bleach — but there are for sure some health risks associated with cholera-laden water. Bleach is also very inexpensive, less than $1 per gallon. Don't use scented bleaches or "bleach substitute"; they're not the same.

Heavy Metals and Agricultural Chemicals: Filtration systems that remove these contaminants are considerably more expensive than bleach, but if you are concerned that either of these might be a problem it is worth your money to filter by the best means possible. Carbon filters, "reverse osmosis" systems, and distillation — or a combination of the three — can be your best line of defense.

Types of Filtration Systems

Katadyn portable water filter.
Courtesy of Lehman's, Kidron, OH. (330) 857-5757.

Portable "ceramic" filters are available for camping trips or extreme circumstances — the Katadyn brand has one for $100 that will filter up to 5000 gallons. Production of clean water is slow, about 1 to 2 quarts per hour, but you can be certain of the quality of your water under any circumstances.

Various under-counter and above-counter filter systems exist that fit "in line" on your water pipes. The costs and reliability vary significantly, along with the ease of use. While it's impossible to cover all the brands, sizes, applications, and their efficiency, here's a set of guidelines when you are shopping:

1. How many gallons can this device filter per hour?
2. Do filter elements need to be replaced? If so, how often?
3. Does the system allow unfiltered water to pass through after elements are used up? If so, this system must be carefully monitored so you can replace elements at the right time.
4. What does the system purify? If the filtration system's main claim to fame is that your water will "taste better," don't bother with it — unless you enjoy good-tasting parasites and bacteria.
5. How much expertise does it take to install this unit?
6. What replacement parts should I have on hand for emergencies?

Water, Water Everywhere...

Backup systems are the secret to success with water acquisition and storage. It never hurts to have several dozen gallons of store-bought spring water tucked away in the basement or garage, *just in case*. Then, if your favorite system breaks down for any reason, you'll still have a clean, drinkable supply until things get back in order.

Chapter Four
Cookin' With Gas... And Wood... And More...

Food occupies a surprising amount of our time, our thoughts, and our energies. It's only after consuming a warm, tasty meal that any of us can fully relax at the end of the day. But if cooking that dinner is complicated by a lack of reliable heat, then you're stuck with cold canned beans — better than starving, but mighty unsatisfying.

A friend recently acquired a new propane-powered stove as a protection against our frequent power-outages. She planned to spend those power-gone evenings baking "Blackout" cookies with her young children to help them understand that power outages weren't a big scary deal. Imagine her dismay when the power went out and the stove wouldn't light! It turned out that the stove had an electricity-powered feature that controlled the gas flow. No power, no gas, no food, period.

Thank goodness there are a pile of alternatives. Chances are good that you've already got the makings of a perfectly useable cooking system somewhere around your place. We'll spend this whole chapter on stoves and cooking methods.

Wood

Probably the most ancient and easily acquired cooking system is one that uses burning wood as the heat source. Campfires, pit-ovens, wood stoves, and even barbecues use either dried collected wood or previously charred wood (charcoal) for heat.

Campfires consist of any small controlled ground-surface blaze that is used for heat and cooking. At its most basic, a spot is cleared on the ground (making sure that nothing flammable, such as tree leaves, are overhead), kindling is lit (newspapers, dry sticks, dry leaves, etc.), and the fire is gradually "fed" larger dry pieces of wood until it sustains itself at a specific level. A backyard campfire is just as good a cooking medium as one deep in the backwoods.

To cook over a blaze, you would need fire-proof pots (cast iron is most reliable) and some means of suspending them above the fire. Real Goods carries a cast-iron set of "camp irons" ($80), consisting of a rod to drive into the ground, a pot hanger, and a 12" x 12" grill, that are portable but heavy at almost 12 pounds. They should last for generations.

With a little thought, it becomes evident that putting dry rocks or bricks around a campfire will help to hold the heat and protect the flame from breezes. Just make sure the rocks aren't from riverbeds or damp — steam buildup can cause these rocks to shatter or explode! If you can stack the rocks on two sides, you can balance an ordinary oven shelf across them to use as a grill surface. Furthermore, the edges of a campfire — where coals and hot ash hold the heat at a fairly even temperature — make ideal places to toss unpeeled potatoes and corn still in the husk, or to nestle the coffee pot.

One of the hardest things to cook well over alternative stoves is pasta — believe me, I have tried. With an open-fire situation, I'd suggest putting your deepest, heaviest pot directly into glowing (but not flaming) coals. Pile coals around the edges and fill the pot with water. When the water boils, add your pasta and watch closely — they'll be done in five minutes or less. Scoop out or drain quickly.

Yeast breads are another campfire trick... there's a reason "pan cakes" and "hush puppies" were invented, and it has to do with the difficulty of getting the dough to rise properly around an uneven campfire. The secret to success is a "Dutch oven" cast-iron pot with a lid, a bed of hot coals, and a layer of ash. After the dough has been kneaded, grease or oil your Dutch oven and place the dough in it. Set this without a lid near your campfire, where the air feels warm but not hot. Rotate the Dutch oven every fifteen minutes or so, letting the sides gently heat. The dough should begin to rise fairly quickly with this treatment. Don't let it get above the lid level. Once the dough has risen, grease the inside of the lid and cover the Dutch oven. Scrape a slight depression in an ashy area next to your fire and put hot coals in this area. Cover the coals with about an inch of warm ash. Put your Dutch oven on top of this. Pile a layer of ash around the oven, and cover this with coals. Add another layer of ash. Basically, you've just supplied an even, warm heat around your Dutch oven that will cook your bread uniformly. Uncover and check the bread in 35 to 50 minutes.

Pit Ovens are literally nothing more than a hole or trench in the ground. Dig your hole about two times the size of whatever you plan to cook and at last one foot deep (two is better). If you want to cook a chicken, for example, you'd need a hole about 20 inches long by 12 to 24 inches deep. A pair of chickens would need a 30-inch by 24-inch trench.

Light a good blaze either in the hole or immediately beside it, and let this burn down to bright hot coals in the bottom of the hole, about 2-4 inches deep. Spread this evenly in the trench. Pile ash and dry dirt on this about one to two inches deep. Wrap your dinner in wet brown bags or aluminum foil, or place in covered pots (bananas leaves, if you've got them, are an ideal wrap). You can even coat foods with an inch-thick layer of clean mud or clay, if you've got nothing else. Put this in the bottom of the hot pit. Cover with ash, coals, and dirt, in that order.

Now, get busy with something else for four or five hours. Ignore the delicious aroma seeping from the ground. After five hours or so, open the pit. Wrapped foods will be deliciously slow-steamed; clay items will be rock-hard and need to be cracked or split open. Incredible!

Wood Cookstoves, like Great-grandma cooked on, are functional, beautiful, inexpensive to operate, and just as fine a device as any gas or electric stove. There are literally hundreds of styles and designs still being made in the US and overseas; new ones run high at about $1000 to $3500. In my area, you can find good-quality older wood cook stoves for around $300 — we got our 1930s model by trading our electric refrigerator for it when we went off the grid. You'll need a chimney with any of these, which can run an additional $150 to $300. If you are buying a used older stove, check that the firebox has no overt cracks — if so, reject it because it will never work right.

Basically, a wood cookstove consists of a box to hold the burning wood; a steel or cast-iron (better) cooktop with removable circular "lids"; an oven; and possibly a water reservoir. When the wood is lit and the stove is closed (except for a vent for air intake), the heat is transferred beneath the cooktop to the chimney. Move a switch, and some of that hot air is channeled around the oven and heats it quickly and evenly. With a little practice, you begin to get a "feel" for your particular stove and its personality. You'll know when to feed it wood and when to open or close the air vents. You'll be able to maintain a surprisingly even and uniform heat through hours of daily use. Keep in mind that you weren't born with this knowledge, either, no matter how educated or sophisticated you are — you've got to learn wood cookstove techniques by doing.

A moderate-sized stove will use two good armloads of wood per day — much of it should be roughly 1" x 2" pieces, about 14" to 16" in length, depending on your firebox. After the stove is going, you can burn big chunks of wood in it.

"Round Oak" porcelain wood cookstove with reservoir. It's had a rough life — lost its feet somewhere (they've been replaced with bricks), and the porcelain is chipping near the handles — but it still cooks and heats all winter long. *Photo by author.*

Wood cookstoves need to be cleaned of their ash buildup about twice a year, generally in spring and before the heavy fall cooking season begins. It's possible to overload the firebox and get a rip-roaring blaze going that threatens to escape into the rest of the house — or that zooms up the chimney like a torch. This is a dangerous situation that can burn down your house. The solution lies in keeping the chimney free of creosote (tarry smoke products) buildup, along with prudent controls over your fire, including the ability to close air-intake vents, and a means to block the chimney itself with a damper. If you're able to close off the air to the fire, that will suppress it quite efficiently. Keep a small fire extinguisher close at hand, and a box of baking soda as well. Don't throw water on any hot cookstove — the temperature change can crack or warp the metal in an instant.

As you might imagine, during the summer a wood cookstove is just as warming as it is in the winter — an undesirable feature in most homes. It's very easy to water-bath-can pickles, jams, and most fruits on a wood cookstove, if you can stand to keep it going at a hot temperature while your water boils. Canning on a cookstove works most comfortably when it is done in the wee cool hours of morning — or if the stove can be transported outdoors to a covered "summer kitchen" type of area. I use a two-burner propane stove that originally was in an RV, for my canning purposes, and for most cooking during the hottest months. The rest of the time, the wood stove cooks for us and keeps us warm.

Barbecues, from the simplest $10 metal pan with a grill to the super-duper $300 propane models, are excellent outdoor cookers for meats and firm vegetables. They work best with purchased charcoal, but you can burn down your own wood to coals and cook as successfully with that if you don't mind waiting. You can't really boil water (make pasta or coffee), or preserve foods, or bake a decent loaf of bread using a BBQ — and you must NEVER, under any circumstances, use one indoors or in a closed structure such as a camper. (They release odorless, colorless carbon monoxide, which can kill you in hours.) BBQing adds flavor to the foods cooked on it, and it generally takes longer than other "in-house" methods. Severe weather will stop outdoor BBQing, although a covered porch or open garage can serve as a cooking area in a pinch, if you don't mind the interior getting smoked.

Getting Wood: If you live in a rural area, you know how abundant wood is year-round, which isn't the same as saying it is cheap. With a chainsaw ($300+... don't scrimp here — a good saw will spare you a lot of grief) or a wood-cutter's handsaw (Lehman's catalog has them for about $90), you can often supply a winter's worth of wood with a week's worth of effort. You'll also need a sledge-hammer type of tool called a maul to break the wood into stove-sized pieces. Chopping wood isn't exactly the kind of work that people will line up to do, but there is a rough satisfaction in hitting that log end just right so that it cracks straight down the middle. One tip on chopping wood that will protect your shins from flying splits — use an old tire. Put your wood with its "up" end down on the ground inside the circle of that old tire. This keeps the pieces from hurtling away at great force. And if you chop with the direction of growth (that is, driving from the "down" end towards the "up" end), the wood splits easier and cleaner.

Enterprise Monarch wood cookstove.
Courtesy of Lehman's, Kidron, OH. (330) 857-5757.

Sweetheart wood cookstove.
Courtesy of Lehman's, Kidron, OH. (330) 857-5757.

Wood mills and lumber yards sometimes have scrap piles that can be purchased for minimum costs when you do the hauling. If you are in the suburbs or the city, wood can be a costly heat source when you have to buy the stuff. You might consider asking at plant nurseries and at companies that remove trees and tree limbs if you can "dispose" of their excess wood for them. Ordinarily, these companies must pay someone to pick up the cut

___

wood and transport it to a dump site, which also charges a fee. Just be prepared to be available when you are called, so that homeowners don't have a pile of unwanted wood sitting around offending neighbors and "clean streets" ordinances.

Benefits of Cooking with Wood: Principally, the ease of acquiring fuel and the relative familiarity of the stuff. Abundant wood is inexpensive, if you know how to get it. It provides an even heat that can be controlled with practice. Foods cooked with any kind of wood heat have that "little bit extra" in flavor and tenderness. Old wood cookstoves can be found in rural areas relatively inexpensively, and last for generations.

Drawbacks of Cooking with Wood: Unless you actively plan ahead and stock up, you will run out of wood, probably at the most crucial moment. Fires can occur and run out of control. Ash must be removed from stoves daily and safely discarded where lingering coals cannot start fires. Most wood-fired cooking systems take longer to get going than other conventional sources such as propane, and consequently add to the cooking time. You can't pressure-can using wood heat of any type, although you're able to water-bath-can. New wood cookstoves are very expensive, but will never need to be replaced during your lifetime. Some areas have restrictions on stoves and burning, which can add to the cost of chimneys and such.

Gas

There are two types of gas which we'll examine. Propane (also called "LP") and kerosene. "Natural gas" is a little different, and stoves need to be altered slightly to accept it, but it is virtually the same as propane in function. Utility companies also usually pipe natural gas into your residence, whereas propane is stored in a canister on your property and refilled periodically by hand or by the utility company. Natural gas can be disrupted by earthquakes tearing up lines in distant neighborhoods; propane lines are shorter and all on one's own property, and often can be checked by the homeowner.

Propane is a product of petroleum manufacture, an odorless and flammable gas. The kind of propane available to fill 18-gallon RV canisters and those large 100- (or more) gallon cylindrical tanks beside rural homes is naturally odorless; gas companies add an unpleasant sulfurous "rotten eggs" smell to the gas so that leaks will be instantly noticeable. Propane is heavier than air, and will seek low spots — something to keep in mind if you smell a leak. Propane can actually invisibly "puddle."

The simplest propane stove is what is known as a "camp stove," generally having one or two burners. The burner portion is designed to hold a pot or pan above a flame-spreader — and this is virtually identical in design to a common household gas stove. The difference is in structure and durability. Most camp stoves are rather flimsy, even if they are perfectly functional.

Average price at department stores is around $40; Lehman's campstove is cast iron and incredibly durable, but costs almost twice the department-store rate.

Additionally, camp stoves can operate on small 8-ounce "cans" of propane which are available at department stores and camping-supply companies. These small cylinders are incredibly expensive compared to purchasing gas in 18-gallon lots — locally, one 8-ounce cylinder runs about $3, and a fill-up for a portable 18 gallon container (which is forty times as much gas) is about $7. The small cylinders have the advantage of being highly portable and easily disposed.

"RV stoves," the kind of cooking surface found in Recreational Vehicles, are a cross between a "built-in" home stove and a camp stove. The cooktop is generally porcelain and easy to clean, while the hidden under-surface is a typical stove-flame spreader and set of copper gas lines. These come in two-, three-, and four-burner models but the size relative to a home stove is smaller. They can be removed from their built-in site in an RV and used as-is, or installed in any kind of non-flammable surface you choose. New, this kind of cooktop may run $100-125 — but used ones that need a little buffing or pipe replacement can be found quite reasonably. (Mine came from a swap meet for $5.)

Some RV stoves are a miniature combination of cooktop and oven — which can also be readily removed from the RV and used as a portable propane stove. One prominent drawback of these stoves is that the oven won't operate correctly unless there is a "draft" leading away from the rear of the oven — in the original RV site, this draft was created by a small electric fan which was designed to pull gasses out of the vehicle interior and expel them outside the RV. This makes it inconvenient to use the oven within a home (and dangerous, too, unless it is also vented to the outdoors). Solar-powered fans can fit the bill quite nicely, and run about $30.

"Gas" also includes **kerosene** as mentioned earlier — and, yes, Virginia, they do still make kerosene-powered stoves. There are 2- and 3-burner models designed to act as standard in-home cookers, and there are portable types that can be used for emergencies or camping situations.

Kerosene stoves operate by the same basic system that is used in kerosene and oil lamps: a reservoir holds a measured amount of kerosene; a heavy wick inserted in the reservoir directs the kerosene up into the area of the burner; the flame is lit with a match brought near the burner-area of the wick. It's simple to use. The single-burner model uses about one quart of fuel every four hours — which is fine for short-term emergency use, or if you have a large vat of kerosene handy. A week's worth of cooking for a family, about 30 hours, could easily use 4 gallons of kerosene. This cooker costs about $85.

Amish-made "Perfection" kerosene cookstoves (see Lehman's catalog) are the same style as the old-farmhouse Perfections, and the parts are interchangeable if you are renovating an old stove. Two or three burners, porcelain finish, and standard stove-flame adjustments make this type of stove as easy to use as an ordinary kitchen appliance. It burns a gallon of kerosene in about 24 hours — which is four times more efficient than the one-burner model. It also costs more, with 2-burners starting at $550, and 3-burners at about $700.

Perfection kerosene cookstove.
Courtesy of Lehman's, Kidron, OH. (330) 857-5757.

Perfection stoves which are properly set tend to burn fairly cleanly — the odor of kerosene is slight to undetectable.

Benefits of Gas/Kerosene: Easy to use, relative familiarity after using oil lamps, moderate cost, emergency applications, excellent cooking and food-heating ability.

Drawbacks of Gas/Kerosene: Need for sturdy storage containers and fireproof storage area, odors, repeated handling and pouring of fuel, disposing of used containers, fire.

...And More

Gas, wood, and electricity are probably the most common cooking-heat sources, but they're certainly not the only means humankind has developed through the ages. Among the modern means are: butane, alcohol, and the sun.

It's ugly and rusty, but it cooks for free. *Photo by author.*

"Butane" stoves are like oil lamps, gas stoves, and most similar to those familiar butane lighters. Real Goods' "Glowmaster" is a single-burner lightweight (5 pounds) butane stove, as useful for emergencies and outdoors cooking as any camp stove. The fuel comes in 8-ounce canisters ($3 each), but may not be immediately available at department stores or camping outlets — if you go this route, it would be wise to stock up (the fuel doesn't "go bad"). The stove runs around $70.

But suppose, in spite of all your preparations, you're at Aunt Zelda's house when the long-predicted Big One hits. Aunt Zelda, bless her heart, hasn't prepared for anything since World War II — and everybody is starting to get hungry. Now what?

If you can scrounge a roll of toilet paper, a tin can large enough to hold it, and a bottle of rubbing alcohol, then you will have the makings of a clean, hot, perfectly useable (if pretty crude) stove.

"Alcohol stoves" are made by putting the roll of TP into the can, and saturating it completely with the isopropyl alcohol — 70% will work, but 90% gives the best results. CAREFULLY touch a match to the top of this, and *voilà* — a beautiful blue flame, hot enough to boil a coffee pot of water in ten minutes or less. You can snuff this flame by completely covering the can with a pot so that air cannot reach the flame. The unused alcohol will keep for short periods if allowed to cool and then covered to slow down evaporation.

People who live on yachts and cook aboard ship may have alcohol-based stoves aboard — marine-supply houses sometimes carry actual alcohol stoves, with one and two burners. Prices may run $60 to $95.

One of the modern stars of low-cost cooking is the homemade "Solar Oven" and the amazing "Solar Stove." Under proper conditions, oven temperatures can reach 350 degrees and can cook a chicken or a loaf of bread with ease. The stove version can bring a pot of water to boil in 10 minutes or less — these get *really* hot *fast*.

Basically, solar cookers are designed to absorb and direct the sun's rays at a particular area by using reflective surfaces or mirrors. Solar ovens contain the heat within the box, allowing sunlight to also enter directly into the oven through a glass front. The solar stove is a curved surface, like the inside of a basketball (technically, a "parabolic curve"), that directs the sun's rays to a marked point in front of the stove, which is where you hold or place the cooking pot.

In order to cook with either oven or stove, you must "aim" the device directly at the sun. Preheating time is very short for the oven, and the stove heats immediately. Because the sun moves across the sky (or, more properly, the earth turns away from the sun!), you must reset the solar cooker every twenty minutes or so to keep it at its hottest — or, if you're cooking a casserole, you can arrange the cooker so that the sun hits it full force for a period of time, then moves away so that the cooker stays warm but not hot. After some experimentation, you can cook as efficiently and as quickly as if you were working on a standard appliance. Plus, the "fuel" is free **forever.**

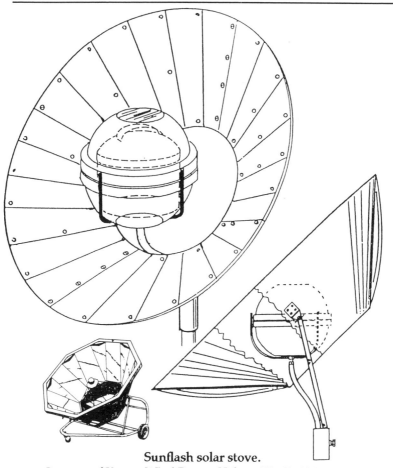

Sunflash solar stove.
Courtesy of Kansas Wind Power, Holton, KS. (913) 364-4407.

Solar ovens are sold through outlets that include Real
Goods, Kansas Wind Power and Lehman's, with prices
from $150 to $200 for the same cooker (shop around!).
This particular model of "Sun Oven" has a fiberglass
body, and weighs 21 pounds. The oven is smallish at
14" h x 14" w x 10" D — but can cook a 12-pound

turkey. Reflective panels surround the glass front, and can be folded down for portability.

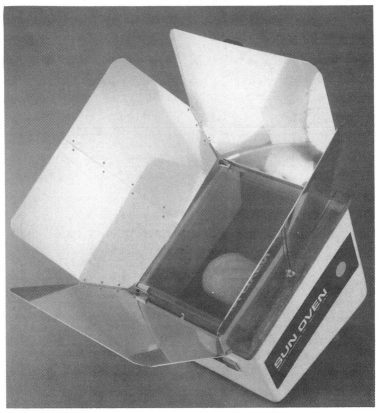

Sun Oven solar cooker.
Courtesy Lehman's, Kidron, OH. (330) 857-5757.

It's surprisingly easy to make a working solar oven or stove, even using very low-cost scrounged materials. Beth and Dan Halacy's *Cooking With The Sun* has several patterns for both, using cardboard, a glass sheet, glue, black tempera paint, tape, and aluminum foil. The first solar oven we made about a decade ago was simply two cardboard boxes nested inside each other, lined with a black plastic bag, and with an old window pane laid across it. We added two pieces of cardboard with aluminum foil (used and re-flattened) stapled to them as reflectors. The total cost for this not-too-attractive item was about 40¢ — but it cooked for us for about three weeks. We had to retire it when the black plastic melted... you can imagine how hot that thing got! Of course, you can make a homemade oven out of better-quality materials, such as plywood or sheet metal, and end up with a very durable portable cooker.

The solar stove is nothing more elaborate than a giant curved reflector, about thirty inches or more around, that focuses the sun on a single spot. Similar parabolic reflectors have actually been used to melt holes through standard steel I-beams, so it's obvious that a tremendous amount of heat must be generated. The Halacys offer specific directions for making this kind of stove out of cardboard and foil — it's incredibly inexpensive, but somewhat time-consuming. You wouldn't want to try to build one during an emergency.

If you can find it, Dan Halacy wrote an earlier book for youngsters entitled *Solar Science Projects* (see Resources). This one is about 25 years old, but loaded with other solar-operated devices you can build at home including a crystal radio, a small solar water heater, and a solar water distiller.

With any solar device, you MUST wear heavy-duty sunglasses while you're nearby — the sun's reflection is painfully sharp and potentially damaging to the interior of the eye (the retina, the part of the eye involved in perceiving images). And, of course, any solar cooker system won't operate at night, when it is heavily overcast, or during storms — though on cloudy days, they do work but not as well.

If you really like the idea of low-cost-fuel cooking and enjoy building things, you can spend next to nothing (if you have the stuff around already) and build a permanent outdoor wood-burning "bread oven." These systems can be as elaborate or simple as you want — and a perfectly useable (though not necessarily permanent) one can be built in a day.

Similar to the primitive ovens in use all over the Third World, this oven can be made using whatever you have on hand. Bricks and concrete give a durable structure; adobe, clay and even mud will work until you get a strong rain.

Basically, this oven consists of a thick-walled chamber with an entrance door and a smoke vent. The interior of the chamber can be nothing more than stone and concrete (of course, firebrick would be the ideal.) The inside of the chamber should be about 15 inches high, and no more than 24 inches long, and slope upward slightly toward the smoke vent. If you can vault the chamber (try building it over a cardboard or metal form) so much the better. Add a piece of stove pipe to draw the smoke up, and top with a covered pipe "hat" if you plan to cook during rainy weather. Include a damper for more control, if you wish. Make the walls of this chamber three to six inches or more thick. You can floor it with your rocks and mortar, if you like, or simply leave the floor as clean packed dirt. The entrance hole should be as small as possible to still allow your typical pans and pots to go in.

Primitive oven. Rock covers entry hole after the fire
is burning and the oven has become very hot.
Illustration by Shary Flenniken.

When the concrete has had a couple of days to cure, you can light your first fire inside the "oven." Put in some dry kindling, touch a match to it, and let it burn. Keep adding wood until you've got a good blaze inside (not so much that flames shoot out your chimney!). Keep the fire fed for about an hour, then rake out and spread your coals around inside. The inside of the oven may be black, or it may have really reached some phenomenal temperatures and burned the soot buildup off the inside masonry. If the oven is floored, you can mop it out with a natural-fiber (not plastic) broom dipped in water — this will steam up the interior, creating the perfect environment for breadbaking. If you have a dirt floor, it'll still bake some mighty fine meals, but don't bother with the mopping. If your oven has a damper, now's the time to close it most of the way. Go ahead and put in your casseroles, bread, roasts, or whatever, and block up the entrance hole — either with stones or a metal plate.

This oven will keep cooking for hours, so have a few things lined up to put in every time you fire it up. Cooking heat radiates off the walls and floor, so cooking times are generally a little shorter than in conventional ovens. And the flavors are superb!

Detailed plans for a build-it-yourself $500 true European-style bread oven can be found in Thom Leonard's *The Bread Book* (see Resources).

So...

I won't repeat my usual suggestion (diversify, diversify, diversify), but I will hint that you will be happier with your cooking system in the long run if you practice with it before you commit to it. Usually, the kind of system we already have experience with is the type that we think of as a "real stove." Also, if the gentleman of the household does the most cooking, I believe he should get to choose the stove system... and if the lady does the cooking, she gets the choice. Cooking takes too much time and personal energy to be doing it on a device you despise, no matter how neat your spouse thinks it is.

Last but not least, if you find yourself in an emergency situation and need to start a fire, *please be certain* there are no gas or propane leaks around BEFORE you strike the first match. Don't be like the guy who smelled a propane leak one night — he was smart enough not to light matches to try to locate the problem. But, flustered at the situation, he stopped to think... and pulled out his pack of cigarettes out of habit.

He lived. But he gave up smoking.

Chapter Five
Heat For A Cold Winter

I live in a big old leaky farmhouse. In the olden days, both cooking and heating were done on a wood stove in the room we now use as a dining room. The walls were nothing more than oak planks overlaid with tar paper, and wind literally whistled in around the window sills. In the winter, it must have been cold enough to freeze water indoors — and, even with our modern improvements, some nights it still is. When you look at old drawings of people in their houses during wintertime, you find that everybody is really bundled up in coats and gloves — indoors. Today, if we feel a draft during the winter while we sit in our socks and T-shirts, we think there's something horribly wrong!

"Insulation" is one of the big differences between then and now. A well-insulated house is easier to heat (and cool) than an uninsulated one, and so costs are significantly less if you have to buy your indoor climate.

Windows are considered one of the major areas of heat loss in both insulated and uninsulated homes. We recently changed from a single-pane window in our bathroom to a double-pane style... for the first time in ten years, the toilet didn't freeze on those sub-zero nights.

Do-it-yourselfers can insulate using batts and blown-in cellulose materials — an average house runs about $500 for either method. Some folks we know are using a longer-term method that costs nothing. Reasoning that blown-in cellulose products are made from "recycled" materials like cotton, polyester and other synthetics, they decided that instead of disposing of used clothing that their children had outgrown and that went badly out of style, they'd fill the air space in their walls with it. It's taken about two years, but their place is nearly done. The only problem they've found is that the material tends to pack down over time and leave an insulation "gap" at the junction of wall and ceiling — so they just keep packing in more!

Window replacement is an excellent do-it-yourselfer weekend project. Replacements, ideally, should be the same size as the windows you are removing — but you can certainly enlarge or reduce the size of the opening if you prefer. But, replacement windows are *expensive*, aren't they? Yes, unbelievably so, if you plan to buy new ones — even vinyl-clad (bottom line) windows will run over $100 each. Here's where your personal recycling skills can earn a small fortune for you. Somewhere in your community, there is a shop that sells used windows. Sometimes, these have come from beautiful old structures that have been demolished, sometimes they're from another residence that has been upgraded. We found our aluminum-clad double-pane bathroom-window-to-be at a "flea market" (used goods) store amid a stack of several hundred other windows. It was complete with screen, clean and ready to install — and cost $15. That's less than a similar size new piece of glass *alone* would have cost. We had to enlarge the wall opening to accept it, so we also used some extra pieces of two-by-four that we had saved from an earlier project — and, admittedly, those two tubes of silicon caulking did set us back an additional $6. We framed the window with one-by-fours ($4) and stained and painted where it needed it ($2). The whole thing cost less than $30 plus a Saturday, and it has saved us a great deal of winter aggravation. It was our first window installation — so easy, and the results were so pleasant that we're planning to install several more "recycled" windows in other parts of the house.

Ways to Achieve Heat

Without the electric company and heat pumps or blowers or central heating, there are three basic ways to produce winter heat: wood, gas, and sun. Of these, wood is the easiest one to supply at home; gas is the most uniform and expensive over the long run; and the sun is the least utilized but requires the greatest changes in your residence.

"Wood" heating, either in a fireplace or heating stove, is reliable, very good at warming air and nearby folks, and acts as a dehumidifier. A standard fireplace will warm a room, but it also sucks warm air out and straight up the chimney — producing a cooling effect. Standard fireplaces, even though they are the most pleasant to sit before and watch, are the very least efficient way to use wood to heat your house.

Jøtul Medium cast-iron heating stove.
Courtesy of Lehman's, Kidron, OH. (330) 857-5757.

Heating stoves are much more efficient at converting lumber to warmth. Cast iron, in particular, is superb at holding and dispersing heat. The heavier the stove, the greater the heating capacity. A typical new cast iron stove may run around $1000 for air-tight quality models. But new small steel stoves, which heat up and cool off more quickly, can be found new for around $200 (see Resources). Don't forget to check at garage sales, flea markets, and in the classifieds for perfectly good used stoves in the $300 range. If you need to install a chimney, it will run an additional $150 to $300.

If you have a fireplace, it can also be retrofitted with a stove — the benefit is that you don't need to replace the chimney, so there is a decrease in cost versus putting in a stove when there is no chimney present.

Masonry stoves are a marvelous old-style heater that has been updated. They are usually built from the ground up (because they are so heavy) and really require quite a bit of sawing and refilling if you'd like to install one in your home. Typically, a masonry stove is a huge structure, perhaps six to ten feet wide and long, and with a wide chimney area to match. The fire box, though, is comparatively small. The secret to the heating capacity of these stoves is a series of s-shaped curves in the internal chimney area, which effectively capture most of the heat generated by the fire. The heat is passed to the masonry structure, and the result is a very warm giant box that generates heat for hours after the fire has gone out. Additional good news on masonry stoves is that they are very economical on wood use — principally because they're able to generate so much heat from the structure. The bad news is that they cost a small fortune to build, typically $6000 to $10,000. Hard-core do-it-yourselfers could probably build one for half that, but there is a real art to building a masonry stove. Check out *Back Home Magazine* in Resources.

A new fad in wood heat is the outdoor stove — a box-like structure about six feet tall and four feet deep and wide, with a feed door and chimney. This stove is baffled so that the smoke leaves through the chimney while the heat is channeled though an underground tunnel or tube into your home. (This requires electric or solar-powered fans to move the air.) These stoves will accept very large pieces of wood, so there's less chopping, and they can be set at a low air-intake level so they burn for twelve to eighteen hours on one fill-up. These stoves also don't add to the dust buildup in your house during the winter. The possibility of fire is significantly reduced because the stove is away from the house. Some applications include a water-heating feature, so that as the stove provides heat for the house, it also warms your bathwater.

One problem the outdoor stove seems to have is the drift of smoke into nearby houses. Since the stove is set on the ground and the smoke rises from about eight to ten feet off the ground, in windy conditions it travels laterally — right to your backdoor. Typically, these stoves can be constructed from a kit for about $2000.

Wood stoves need to be cleaned of internal ash and wood-tar (creosote) buildup once or twice a year, most often in fall and spring. Also, indoor models need to have ash removed on a daily basis while they are in use.

One stove to be wary of is the alcohol-fueled "fireplace" that can be installed without a chimney. These cost around $300 and produce a pretty flame —

but they really are just for decoration. The heat-producing capability is small. If you want one of these, by all means get one, but don't expect it to keep you toasty when the wind howls and snow piles up on the porch.

"Buying wood" can be the most expensive way of getting your fuel, but you may need to do it at some point in your heating career. Typically, firewood is sold by the rick (or rank), an amount which translates to: a level pickup bed load, or a stack which is 4 feet by 8 feet by 16 or 18 inches wide. Local definitions for a rick or rank will vary somewhat, and also vary by sellers — some call a stack which is 8 feet by 8 feet by 18 inches a rank, and some call it a cord (locally, its a cord). You'll want to ask the seller for his or her definition of the quantity they are offering. Wood prices are fairly low out here in the sticks, running about $20 to $25 per rank delivered; less than 200 miles away in a city, the same wood sells for $35 per rank. Most deliveries usually require that you buy a minimum of three (3) ranks at a time.

Inspect the quality of the wood before you buy it. Features which are desirable are: wood is already split into stove-sized pieces (which usually runs up the price); wood straight-grained if it is not split (which makes it easier for you to split); and wood is not green, sappy, or wet (which means it needs to sit around for a couple of months in order to burn well). The best woods for heating are hardwoods: oak, hickory, nut trees such as walnut and pecan, and fruitwood such as apple or pear. Fast-growing trees burn all right, but they don't provide a long burn. These include: poplars and cottonwoods. You should probably try to avoid using pines and cedars if possible, since they generate an extremely hot but short heat and create a heavy creosote buildup. These resinous woods are very good for getting a fire going, though, if not too much is used at one time. Some wood sellers will offer mill ends and odd-sized pieces — these burn just as well as any other wood, but you should be certain the piece sizes will fit into your stove.

Benefits of Wood Heat: Easy to find stoves and equipment, familiar, relatively easy to use. Relatively inexpensive fuel (free, if you've got woods, a good saw, and some time on your hands); truly warming heat that is comfortable and drying. The drying quality can be ameliorated somewhat by keeping a kettle of water on the stove to produce steam.

Drawbacks of Wood Heat: Fire: Chimney and flue fires. Ash disposal (try putting it in the garden and around fruit trees — they love the potash); dust and fine ash in the home air is very hard on people with lung ailments; initial costs of new stoves and associated constructions.

Gas, Propane, Kerosene

Gas and propane will be considered to be identical for our purposes; they use the same types of stoves with only a small air-intake adjustment. The main difference between natural gas and propane is the delivery system — natural gas comes through pipes from a utility company, whereas propane is stored in a tank on your property and is delivered there by a utility company truck twice a year. Either way, you've got to purchase your fuel. At this time, propane is about 80¢ per gallon — a five-hundred-gallon tank runs about $400 to fill, and will last about six months of ordinary usage.

Gas stoves come in all shapes and styles. They are efficient, produce a pleasant and warming heat, and can be thermostatically operated (an electric hookup or continuous battery connection is required) so the heat can be kept uniform day and night. There is some dust associated with gas heat, and there is also a little indoor air-pollution in the form of carbon monoxide generated. Gas stoves also need a chimney or outside vent. Typically, these stoves are installed and hooked up by the utility company at little or no charge, but the stoves when new run $600-800. Used gas stoves should be thoroughly checked by utility personnel before being hooked up to the gas lines. Utility guys have special equipment to sense the gas leaks that you can't see. Wood stoves have a certain leeway in usage, but you don't want to be sloppy or casual anywhere that gas is used.

Gas stoves should be professionally cleaned and inspected at least once a year — most people seem to do this in the fall.

Kerosene heating stoves are another story entirely. There are types of kerosene heaters that are vented to the outdoors in much the same way as wood or gas heaters, and which are just as safe. Prices for new ones run around $500. They also are available as portable models for about $150, which are supposed to be used in well-ventilated spaces like garages, but are often kept indoors instead — a potentially fatal mistake! Carbon monoxide is produced copiously, along with burning products that can irritate people with lung ailments.

The big difficulty with kerosene heat is that it is very smelly. Additionally, it's too easy to spill fuel oil accidentally when pouring it into the stove tank — and the mess is hard to clean off the carpet and wood floors.

Benefits of Gas and Kerosene: Easy to find fuel, fuel sources, and assistance. Gas is relatively clean-burning and even-heating. Costs for stoves are moderate to expensive; fuel is moderate.

Drawbacks of Gas and Kerosene: Fire. Explosion. Carbon monoxide poisoning. Possibility of supply being disrupted during emergency or severe weather situations, dependence on utility companies and the skill of their personnel. Cost over time may vary significantly and without warning.

Using the Heat of the Sun

There is an entire industry involved with developing uses for the sun's heat, and innovations pop up almost every day, if you know where to find them. One of the most fundamental features of sun-heating is that it is actually quite easy to capture. Just think of your garden hose after it has laid out in the sun during the summer — the water comes out hot enough to scald, which is to say, well over 120° F.

Now, if you apply that simple physics lesson to heating your house, you'll see that any large area that is exposed to sun AND that can retain that heat is the essence of a sun-heating system.

A Trombe wall. Masonry wall facing the sun is painted flat black. Low vents allow cool floor-level air to flow between the masonry and a heavy glass panel. Air heats in the confined space, rises, and re-enters the house from the top vents near the ceiling.
Illustration by Shary Flenniken.

With this idea in mind, you can understand some of the plans that came out of early solar studies. One of these was the Trombe Wall (named after a Dr. Trombe who invented it) which consists of a large glass sheet spaced four or five inches away from a masonry wall. The masonry has several holes near the base and several more near the ceiling. The back of the masonry wall faces into your room, and the glass-fronted side faces toward the sun and is painted a flat black to absorb as much heat as possible.

The glass retains heat as the masonry warms up. Hot air begins to move out the upper holes into your room — and pulls cool floor-level air from your room through the lower holes into the space to be heated. This then rises, passes into your room and draws more cool air into the system. The whole setup is very elegant in its simplicity, requires no electricity or supplementary energy, and heats in a way that is nearly miraculous in its efficiency.

However (and there's always a "however"), the Trombe Wall does cost to set up — even if you use Plexiglas, old windows, or other salvaged goods. It must be airtight so that you're not incidentally drawing cold air in from outdoors through cracks. And, if you don't have clear sunny days, the heat output is reduced. Finally, an earthquake, hail storm, or even strong winds could put the Trombe Wall out of business indefinitely by cracking the glass.

Similar to the Trombe Wall is a system designed and explained in *The Mother Earth News* (Resources, of course). This is a window-mounted "sun grabber" — a box that operates on the same principle as the Trombe Wall, cycling air out of a cool room into the box to be heated, and then returning it to the room as warm air.

This system would cost less than $100 to build if you bought all the materials new, and could heat a room as long as it lasted without any additional fuel costs. We once heated bathwater in plastic trash barrels, by placing the dark brown barrels in the summer sun. Suppose you took a number of metal barrels, filled them with water, painted the barrels flat black, and set them beside a south-facing window... you'd get an efficient source of heat that would stay warm and radiate heat into any nearby space. The quantity of water would tend to cool slowly, so heat is actually retained and released overnight from a system like this one. You'd need a large window and the willingness to give up your view in exchange for heating — but you'd probably be able to "recycle" the rest of the materials needed for this system. At night, you'd want to be able to close the window with insulated curtains so little of your precious heat would be lost.

People with greenhouses can capture the heat of that system in black-painted barrels filled with water, which are kept beneath your planting bench. In spring and fall, the barrels retain heat and extend your greenhouse season and plant production.

A review of the literature on solar heating will provide you with dozens of ideas and many other possibilities. Just remember that you will probably want a back-up system, in case the sun is obscured for any length of time.

This greenhouse traps heat in the black-painted, water-filled barrels. At night, that heat is released back into the air, warming plants and extending your growing season.
Illustration by Shary Flenniken.

Benefits of Solar Heating: Very clean, no dust and very little daily maintenance. Excellent heating capacity when the sun shines. Fuel is free forever.

Drawbacks of Solar Heating: Can be expensive to set up. Requires designs specific to your home and property. Doesn't work at night (when it is coldest), and when sun is obscured for long periods of time. Systems may be shattered or broken by emergency situations.

A Cautionary Word about Pellet Stoves

The pellet stove, a highly efficient system which burns manufactured marble-sized pellets of wood products, is often heralded as the heater of the future. Pellet stoves use materials which might otherwise be wasted, and have catalytic converters on their chimneys that limit polluting burning products, so they are ecologically sound. They're relatively inexpensive to operate because they are so efficient — some use no more than a couple of pounds of pellets per day to heat a room to a toasty warmth. And some models can be converted to burn whole corn, in case you've got a crop excess and no way to sell it. They're often no more expensive than a new wood-burning heater.

The primary drawback of these otherwise excellent stoves, as far as I am concerned, is the pellets. I can't grow pellets — I'd have to buy them forever. If I am in an emergency, I can't go down to my neighborhood feed store or supermarket and pick up some pellets. Burning whole corn? During the 1930s Depression, some Mid-western grain producers heated their homes with whole corn — it was worth less than wood at the time. But as I am writing, we are facing a marked increase in grain prices brought about by drought, plant disease, and storage shortages. By this winter, a fifty-pound bag of corn may cost three times what it did last year — and the year after that is anybody's guess. I hope for better harvests and filled grain bins, but in the meantime I'm sure not going to install a heater than requires *food* to keep me warm.

Chapter Six
Keeping Cool And Collected

Long before "air conditioning" was even thought of, people living in the hottest climates in the world were keeping cool and comfy during the blazing days of summer. Arab princes were good examples — in spite of the desert environment, water shortages, and lack of what we'd consider suitable building materials, they kept their elaborate palaces cool. Their system worked so well that ancient structures in the Middle East *still* stay cool in the summer, long after their builders have been gone and forgotten.

Similarly, native tribes of the Southwest in the US and Mexico constructed dwellings that were comfortable in both the heat of summer and freezing cold of desert winters. If you are fortunate enough to enter one of these homes, either a private home or in a reconstructed historical site, it is always a surprise how comfortable they are.

The construction "secret" of these dwellings was *mass*, the same characteristic we found so important in solar-heating applications. For solar heat, the mass of a quantity of water was used to "store" heat — and in those desert dwellings that stay so cool, stone, rocks, and adobe provide a large quantity of mass that retains coolness even when the sun is burning hot. Walls on these buildings are frequently eighteen to twenty-four inches thick, and sometimes as much as three feet in thickness. For Arab sheikdoms, these walls also provided fortresses against invaders' arrows and cannon shots.

But there are other things you can do, if your home isn't made like a British castle.

Once Again, Insulation

A well-insulated house has a "dead space" between outside weather and inside temperatures. This space may be created by blown-in cellulose, batting, trapped air, or any number of materials — but its function is the same: to prevent the free movement of heat through it. *Anything* that slows that movement also acts as insulation.

One popular building style for homesteaders is "straw bale" construction. Literally using bales of old hay or fresh straw, walls are laid up on a concrete foundation course and secured in place using steel wires. Windows and doors are wood framed. The straw is covered with chicken-wire mesh and plastered with any number of mortar-like materials to provide an outside weatherproofing and an inside regular "wall." This type of housing can last for a generation or longer, and — if done properly — is no more prone to fire than a wooden house. But the thickness of the walls (16" to 20") makes them incredibly insulated and keeps the internal temperatures fairly constant.

"Underground" and "basement" houses — ones which have their first regular floor underground — are also superbly insulated by the thick layer of soil around the outer walls. Often, underground homes need no additional summer cooling, except perhaps a small fan to move air through the structure... and not even that if the place has been constructed to take into account prevailing local winds. In the winter, a single cookstove (wood or gas) keeps the dwelling plenty warm.

Cooling From the Earth

There's no reason why modern homeowners couldn't take another lesson from Arabia — indoor "air conditioning" from the ground. Using the same principles that we'll see in the next chapter on keeping food cool, this kind of cooling is based on another well-known law of physics: warm air rises, and cool air falls.

Desert palaces, before abundant electricity and central heating and cooling, depended on underground tunnels to supply their cold air. Here's how it worked: when the palace was constructed, long lines were laid out away from the building like spokes coming off the center of a wheel. These lines were then dug into trenches several feet deep, which might vary from 3 to 7 or 8 feet deep by a foot or two wide (depending on the size of their laborers). In the bottom of these trenches, clay cylinders were placed, forming a long tube. The far end of this tube turned and rose above the ground level and had some type of porous cap placed in it. As the line of the tube neared the palace, its level in the soil gradually rose until it entered the building's walls. Air vents in the walls opened at about floor height, which was higher than the main line of the tube, but lower than the outside opening at the far end of the tube.

Cooling from the earth, palace-style.
Illustration by Shary Flenniken.

This non-electrical form of air conditioning operated because of the movement of air through the system — the coldest air was in the deepest part of the trench. The floor-level air vent released slightly warmed air that had flowed upward from the deepest level — which then drew in heated outside air through the far end of the tube. During hot weather, the constant "draw" from inside the dwelling would continue to move air from outside, through the trench where it cooled, and then into the palace. With several dozen of these tubes operating continuously, your residence would be comfortably cool no matter what the outside thermometer read.

To "turn off" this system, you'd only have to cap the outside intake vent and the air movement would stop. Of course, in the winter, the deepest levels of ground stay about 55 degrees — so maybe this type of system could be used to "pre-warm" house air in the same fashion. Modern builders and retrofitters could speed up the building process by using a backhoe and plastic pipes, but the basic idea remains the same.

The Cooling Power of Wind

We have come so far from basic contact with nature in our society, that we've virtually forgotten the fundamentals of reality. For example, when my family raised rabbits in Southern California, we would generally lose a few in the summer — the bunnies couldn't take the intense heat. Rabbit-raising friends suggested we keep them in a cool garage (we didn't have one) or that we periodically spray the rabbits with cold water. Well, the rabbits didn't care for the wet coats or being hosed down a couple of times a day, so we tried to think of another option. Sure enough, when you're looking for ideas, you tend to find them — an old neighbor mentioned that when he was a boy, his parents would soak their curtains during the hot part of the day, and let the wind bring water-cooled air into the house through the windows. By evening, the curtains were dry and the house was tolerably cool.

Effectively, we'd been doing the same thing with the rabbits when we soaked their coats — the animals kept cool as long as air moved through the wet hair and evaporated off along with body heat. We've all had the same experience after swimming when your T-shirt is wet. Even on a hot day, wind movement makes you feel significantly cooler as your shirt dries out. So, we went ahead and tried hanging wet cloth along the sides of the rabbit cages. We found that burlap, with its porous texture and ability to hold water, worked the best. The rabbits were comfortable, we were happy, and a new/old method of keeping cool was remembered and put to use.

Using Shade

Here's another thing we've nearly forgotten — people once planted trees around their houses *not* for looks but for *shade*. Although most modern landscaping is designed for "focal points" and "curb appeal," trees still provide some of the most potent temperature reducers the world has ever known. The old oak tree leaning protectively over Grandpa's house kept the place cooler in summer — and warmer in winter — than it would have been without the pleasant shade (and probably provided some protection from lightning, as well!).

But Grandpa didn't plant a 50-foot-high tree. He planted an acorn when he was a boy, and by the time he was an old gent that acorn was doing the job it was intended to do. Today, we don't plan 50 years ahead — we want our shade tree NOW!

Well, if you are willing to invest five years instead of fifty, you can have excellent shade anyway. Fast growers like columnar hybrid poplars, and shade-form hybrid poplars, can put on eight feet of growth annually, reaching about 40 feet tall in just a few years. We planted both types of hybrids on the extremely hot west side of our old farm house. Five years ago, these trees were just three-foot-tall sticks. Today, they are towering above the roof of the structure, and the formerly hot west side is now a comfortable and shady garden.

Hybrid poplars are inexpensive (you can sometimes find them on sale for $2 each), they are seldom bothered by insect pests, they will flourish just about anywhere as long as they get watered regularly for the first two years, and they grow like crazy. In addition, the leaves are favored by sheep, goats and rabbits (and are high protein at 28%), and they can literally be grown from sticks cut off the tree in early spring. In fact, hybrid poplars are so eager to grow that the roots send up energetic root sprouts all over your yard (more for the goats, as we say) and a cut twig will sprout roots if you put it in a jar of water. As a bonus, the poplars have a pleasant flowery aroma in early spring as the leaf buds begin to open.

Poplars of this type have a very short life (for a tree), and generally don't live more than 40 years. They make acceptable firewood — one person suggested planting an acre of columnar poplars spaced on 6-foot centers. After four years, you could harvest a portion of that acre for firewood, and it would regrow by the time you'd harvested off the other portions.

Other fast-growing trees include willows and silver maples. Willows have delicate leaves and narrow branches, but can also grow at phenomenal rates. One hybrid willow being marketed as "Austrees" can put on 10 feet of growth or more annually. Silver maples also grow rapidly, perhaps five to six feet yearly. They are "tapable" trees that can yield sap to boil down into maple syrup. For syrup, trees should have a trunk that is no less than 7 inches in diameter — but it only takes a few years for these fast-growers to get there. Silver maples turn yellow in the fall rather than the fiery red you'd expect of a maple, and they are brittle trees — branches break off in high winds and during ice storms. Both willows and maples are relished by livestock, and willow leaves can also provide an aspirin-like tea that is used to relieve aches and pains and to lower fevers.

But supposing you need shade THIS YEAR, then what? Then, turn to vining plants. If you choose your vines carefully, they can produce a temperature-reducing effect indoors, while also providing nutritious food. In California, we grew grape vines along a trellis on the south side of our house. The heat seemed to stimulate the vines to grow really well, so we had a wall that was green with leaves and seedless grapes. By winter, the leaves had died back and left the walls open to the warming sun.

In temperate climates where you don't get a late frost, an incredibly productive plant is the "chayote" (pronounced chay-oh-tee or shay-oh-tee) or "alligator pear." These incredible gourd-relatives can grow 100 feet in a single season. They flower and fruit quite late, beginning to set fruit around September, but every vine will be covered with the pear-shaped green or white things. The fruit is something like a squash in flavor and texture when cooked, and they make excellent pickles when a "bread and butter" sweet recipe is used. And, they only have around 25 calories per chayote. You can't eat them raw, though, unless you enjoy mucilaginous textures and tree-bark firmness. You can grow a plant from a single chayote fruit — just put the fruit in a plastic bag kept at room temperature. Roots will form from the wide bottom end in about ten days, and the whole thing can then be planted shallowly in good damp soil. These plants are fairly shallow-rooted, so if you have very hot and drying weather, they'll do better with a thick mulch and frequent nighttime watering. Some strains of chayotes require male and female plants, and some are self-fertile.

Chayotes are very frost-sensitive and will die back to the ground in winter. In areas that hardly ever get below freezing, these plants can overwinter in the ground under thick mulch — after several years, they will have a large sweet-potato-like root that is also very tasty. In addition, the leaves, stems and twining tendrils are also edible. The stem tips taste a little like asparagus. Train the fast-growing stems up a trellis on the side of your house and you'll have heat protection in about a month.

In regions that have more severe winter weather, one of the best fast-growing vines that also produces quality food is the Chinese kiwi fruit. These are a little different than the fuzzy brown ones you can find in the supermarket. The Chinese (also called Manchurian or Siberian) variety produces a grape-sized fruit with the same spritely strawberry/banana flavor, but which is smooth skinned and green colored. In the spring, the plants are covered with fragrant blossoms, and by the fall they have hundreds of these excellent fruits clinging all over the vine. A mature (5- to 7-year-old) plant can easily produce ten gallons of fruit — which makes fine quality jams, jellies, syrups, etc., and which can be kept in cool storage for six weeks.

Kiwis require both male and female plants in order to produce fruit — except for one variety known as Issai. Issai are self-fertile, but they also seem to be somewhat less hardy than the Chinese variety. Chinese kiwis can tolerate winter temperatures of 20° below zero. Kiwis do require a very sturdy and heavy trellis, though — the weight of the fast-growing vine will crush poorly made and flimsy supports.

Where vines are concerned, don't forget the flowering plants that can grace a hot sun-facing wall. Morning glories, Virginia creeper, ivies, and other favorites make excellent heat-reducers while making the side of your house more attractive as well. If you have children, avoid plants that have potentially poisonous berries or leaves (such as morning glories with their toxic seeds).

Trellis can be incredibly expensive and elaborate ($200-$300) or can be made from sections of wire fence nailed to the side of your house. We've used the heavy-gauge "cattle panels" (12 feet long and about 4 feet wide) as trellis supports — new, they run about $16 and can be curved and bent over an area like an arch if you wish to have that sort of thing. Cattle panels last for years and years.

Keep it Moving

Heat doesn't have to become something you dread. If it's 95 degrees outdoors and 80 degrees indoors in the summer, that's a significant temperature difference. You might not feel like doing aerobics at 80 degrees, but you could take care of your regular daily activities with minimal discomfort.

If there is some way you can keep indoor air moving, you'll feel even more comfortable. When building a home, put windows where the prevailing wind can enter and leave. Make your eaves twice the size your plans suggest and you'll add shade and protection as well. Twelve-volt and solar fans are ideal additions during this time of year, and often give just enough air movement to keep you really at ease.

Move your bed to the coolest room in the house (who cares what the neighbors think!), and you'll come through hot weather without too many complaints.

Chapter Seven
Refrigeration And Frozen Goodies, Minus Electricity

Summer or winter, we are a culture that is dependent upon the cold to preserve our foods. This includes simple cooling, as we might find in a refrigerator, and the long-term food-keeping that takes place with a freezer. In some parts of the world today, foods are gathered and used on the same day or within several days because refrigeration simply isn't available.

Cold does basically one thing — it prevents bacterial growth and spoilage in foods. Foods left at room temperature begin sprouting all manner of unseen organisms within hours of preparation; it's natural. If you leave foods out overnight without cooling, you run the risk of giving yourself a dose of some interesting intestinal bacteria including: salmonella, serratia, pseudomonas, and even the notorious E. coli, depending on how foods have been handled. All these bugs give you diarrhea — which is often short-lived in healthy adults, but can really wreak havoc with infants, toddlers, sick folks, and the elderly.

Invisible Alternatives

I'm calling these refrigerators "invisible" because they look so much like regular electric refrigerators that you almost can't tell them apart. With a standard freezer above and typical refrigerator below, these are about the size of a small electric fridge. They come in the same "decorator colors" as electric devices, too.

The difference is that these alternative systems operate either on propane, 12-volt direct current batteries, or kerosene. There are a number of brands, some made just as they were a generation ago, some brought in from Europe — and they act just like an electric refrigerator in cooling power. Propane and natural-gas refrigerators use about ten gallons of fuel per week, more or less, which works out to about $12 per month to keep these running. It seems odd, but you must light a flame inside this refrigerator to keep your food cold. Kerosene refrigerators operate by the same method.

These appliances are not inexpensive. You should plan to spend $2000 plus shipping to acquire a standard-size gas or oil refrigerator bought new. Occasionally, you can find a used one for sale for around $300 — but usually these are snapped up as fast as they come on the market. You need to check the wick periodically and input system, but the dangers of these are the same as with any appliance which uses potentially explosive fuels. Most also need regular defrosting.

Battery-powered refrigerators are small — about the size of a large picnic cooler — and perfectly portable. The popular models plug into your car battery through the cigarette lighter, and can keep foods about 40 degrees cooler than outside temperatures. You can also operate these from standard electric current with an additional adapter, so products can be kept cool during transit by plugging into the car, and then plugging into the house current when you get where you are going. Built-in RV refrigerators also operate on the RV's batteries, which are a somewhat larger collection of batteries than an ordinary car has. One of these small battery refrigerators run about $100 or less; used RV fridges can be found very inexpensively, and new ones may run less than $200.

Benefits of "Invisible" Alternatives: No electricity, good cooling capacity, frozen foods can be kept indefinitely, fuels routinely available.

Drawbacks of "Invisible" Alternatives: Fuels potentially dangerous, need to be monitored from time to time, defrosting necessary. Cost is significantly higher than electric models.

The Famous Ice-Box

You can still find old ice-boxes at antique shops and in old houses. They are often very sturdily made, heavy, and metal-lined as a means of retaining the cold. And, all have a section at the top to hold the big block of ice that provided the cooling power of these systems. They require absolutely no energy input.

Of course, ice melts. A drip pan collects the cool water beneath to prevent overflows. A single block might last from three days to almost a week, if the door isn't opened very often — every time you open the door, cold is lost from the system, and the ice melts a little more quickly.

The cooling capacity of an ice-box is fair, compared to the appliances we are familiar with. It won't keep frozen items (like ice cream) in a frozen condition. Foods which go into the ice-box warm draw a great deal of cooling capacity from other foods stored in the system — so there is some temperature variability in the contents. The ice itself may become a problem during emergency situations... somebody has to go out and get a block of ice every few days. The original ice-box became a kitchen feature during a time when ice deliveries were made directly to people's homes — without those frequent deliveries, the system is more inconvenient to operate.

During the winter, you can make your own ice by placing "PAM"-spray-coated bread pans, filled with water, out in a sheltered area to freeze. Take those conveniently sized blocks and use them in your ice-box. Unfortunately, you really need your ice-box more in the summer when ice is harder to come by!

You can also make an ice-box at home using several layers of plywood sandwiched around Styrofoam insulation. Make sure the door latches tightly and that you open it infrequently. Don't forget that we already have a modern equivalent to the ice-box in those picnic coolers. One cooler really doesn't store enough cold to be efficient (the ice melts in a day or so), but nesting a smaller cooler inside a larger one will provide greater insulating and cooling capacity.

Holes in the Ground

In the US, we often find older homes that are equipped with large ice boxes, which are incorporated into the house structure — we call them "fruit cellars" or "basements." Generally, if these are fairly well-constructed and have some kind of useable air-venting system, they stay cool enough to keep vegetables crisp and prevent milk from souring for a few days. Typically, the temperatures will range from about 40° in winter to about 65° in summer.

If you already have a basement area, you can readily partition off a portion using two-by-fours and plaster-board. Construct this on the side of the house that faces away from the sun, and in the coldest corner of the basement. Include a vent that draws air in near the basement floor and another that lets warming air out at ground surface.

Some older farms still have useable "spring houses," a basement-like structure that actually has a small brook running through it. These springs keep quite cool year around. Food items can be placed in containers and then set into the running water — and the cooling power of this medium is excellent. Spring houses were used to keep milk cool by the same method. The air in spring houses, as you might expect, is quite damp, so anything that doesn't like humidity shouldn't be stored in a spring house.

Additionally, that beautiful, clear running water may be loaded with bacteria — don't put unprotected food directly into the water, or wash food in that water without having it tested. (If you have a community or four-year college near you, contact the microbiology professor. First-year micro students often test local waters for "enteric" (intestinal) contaminants and may be willing to use your water for their tests.)

Okay — the power's gone off suddenly, and by the look of things in the world, it'll be off for some time. Lacking a basement or a spring house, what then?

At the frost level in your area — the depth that the ground will freeze down to in winter which is usually three to six feet — the soil remains a cool 55 degrees, on average, year around. In northern climates, it may be a bit cooler, and at the equator it's undoubtedly warmer. If you have a shovel, a strong back, and a 5-gallon plastic bucket, you can make your own cold hole. For speedy storage, move items into the bucket and put it into the ground — then cover with hay or straw or even leaves to make your access easier. (If it rains, you'll have to take out your bucket because the hole will fill with water.) Put your hole underneath a tree in deep shade, or in the center of a cool section of woodland, and it'll keep foodstuffs quite readily for some time.

Dûg holes can meet emergency needs with only the effort to make the hole. If you have an old refrigerator or freezer box with the door still attached, consider burying this for an in-ground cold box. Set the box so that three to four inches of the body remains above ground level so that rain puddles won't run into the box. Put in your cold goods, close the lid, and then cover the top with a couple of feet of dirt, hay, or leaves. For best effects, plant your box underneath a shady tree!

Lacking the means to dig a hole, remember that the crawl space under your house is deeply shaded and significantly cooler than the ambient air temperature.

Holes work because they are cooler than the area above ground — but they simply won't maintain frozen goods for any length of time. If the power goes off and will be off for a long time, eat your ice cream first and then go ahead and use your canning jars to preserve whatever you're able, using propane or wood heat.

The Glorious Cold Shaft

Here's a system that has been all but forgotten as a cool-keeper: the cold shaft. In the desert environment of Southern California, residents in the 1920s built this system right into their houses — and their cold shafts worked to keep apples, vegetables, milk and other products about 30 degrees cooler than outside temperatures.

This is how they were made: an area was selected where the shaft was to open for ready access. This may have been in the kitchen itself, or in a hallway beside the kitchen, but it was also situated near the center of the house. The interior of the shaft was about 16 inches by 16 inches, and the walls of the shaft ran from beneath the floor up through the ceiling into the attic area. The shaft walls were quite thick, at least four inches of wood — but we could easily duplicate these shafts today using plywood and Styrofoam. The shaft's interior walls were metal — probably tin- or zinc-coated — but we could use any oil-based non-toxic "bathroom"-type paint to protect the interior. Cracks should be caulked.

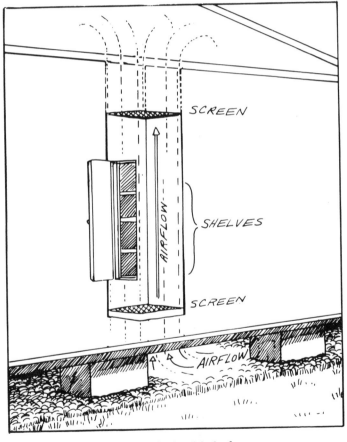

A simplified cold shaft.
Illustration by Shary Flenniken.

The floor hole in the shaft opened into the crawl space and was protected with screen and one-half-inch wire. The shaft had several wire shelves placed about a foot apart so that you could place goods on different levels. And, at the top, the shaft narrowed and opened into a hole in the attic, which was also protected by a heavy screen. A narrow door, thick and heavy to retain coolness, completed the box.

Food stored in the cold shaft was kept in a constant flow of air — the heated attic drew rising air into it and pulled shade-cooled air from the crawl space into the shaft. Even during the hottest part of the day, the crawl-space air was cool enough to keep the foods from wilting.

Beware of vermin and bugs in this system, though — you may need to line your cold shaft with metal screens to keep the critters out.

Chapter Eight
Keeping The Lines
Of Communication Open

If you haven't yet heard, there is nothing quite like the BBC radio. This fascinating English broadcasting system sends its signals worldwide bearing news, sports, informational programs, entertainment, music and so forth — all with that peculiarly British charm and dignity. The BBC can be found on any shortwave radio, at almost any location on the planet, a little corner of oh-so-civilized behavior.

In fact, that same $40 shortwave (Radio Shack's cheapest model, on sale) can bring you Radio China, Radio Cuba, numerous Spanish-language broadcasts from all over the place, Russian stations, India's channels, South African programs, Arabic songs, and even programs from other countries that offer on-the-air language lessons. There are Protestant preachers galore, millenarians, Armageddonists, gold-bugs, UFO-chasers, and a wide section of one band devoted to Catholic programming in numerous languages (have you ever heard the Mass said in Chinese?). Chuck Harder, Rush Limbaugh, Voice of America, George and Gracie reruns, and a militant-feminist person are on at various times in various places. Basically, nearly any subject you may have an interest in can be found at some time on shortwave — you can put your "ear to the world."

Communications of different types take on special emphasis during emergency situations and when you choose to be off the grid. During any kind of calamity, you want to know what's going on: is it only my house, my neighborhood, my town? Is the whole state involved? The whole country? Shortwave reaches outside your area, and with a little button pushing you can quickly assess the situation. If you live in Mule Trail, Kansas, and you hear a report about your emergency on the BBC, you *know* it's a big event!

But any kind of radio, even a little portable AM/FM "Walkman" type, can bring you great assurance or decent entertainment. Costs are relatively small for battery-operated portables (the best kind to have on hand for emergency), ranging from about $15 for AM/FM to the shortwaves in the under-$100 category.

Battery-powered and DC-powered mini-televisions can be found at department stores and Radio Shacks for under $100 for black-and-white models, and for under $200 for LCD-color models. The tiniest screens, about 2", limit viewing to a single person — but if you can't get the news any other way, this certainly works.

For real survival buffs, several models of solar-powered AM/FM radios are available for about $40, and some even have hand-crank features so you can charge them when the sun doesn't shine. Look for a model with a metal crank if you can find one, or plan to replace the plastic crank handle on the model you get — the plastic ones break easily under the pressure of repeated cranking.

Dynamo solar-powered AM/FM radio.
Courtesy of Real Goods Trading Corp., Ukiah, CA. (800) 762-7325.

Talking

Sometimes, you just want to talk to somebody. If a storm has disrupted your phone service, you can still reach the outside world with a CB radio. "Citizen Band" includes channels you can use without acquiring a "ham radio operator's license." CBs are ideal for people who do a lot of driving and for folks with isolated homes, especially for emergency use. Battery-powered CBs are rather large and heavy for hand-held communicators, but the signal does travel for some distance in all directions. They aren't much good for long-range broadcasting, though. A single hand-held portable CB can be found for less than $100. You'll need two if you want to talk to distant family members during hikes or field work.

If you like the idea of not only *listening* to the world, but of *talking back*, you can investigate ham radio. It is not an inexpensive hobby — equipment can set you back hundreds to thousands of dollars, and the really committed (addicted?) ham operators can turn this pastime into a passion. You will need to learn Morse Code and pass several Federal Communications Commission tests for speed before you can actually speak into the airwaves, but even that process can be fun and educational. Ham operators are often pressed into service during disasters to send and receive messages to and from outside the area, and they are well-respected by other emergency personnel.

For very short-range communications of a quarter-mile or less, FM walkie-talkies are both inexpensive (less than $100 for a good pair) and perfectly functional.

Be wary of low-priced no-name imports! Look for equipment that is solidly made and has a brand name you recognize as representing quality (or at least the ability to get your money back). You don't need to buy the top-of-the-line, but bottom-of-the-line will be more trouble than it is worth.

Antennas

You can boost your signal-pickup power, and increase your sending range, by acquiring a good antenna. Some radios come with a 50-foot loop of plastic-covered copper wire, which doesn't seem like much of an antenna until you hook it up to the radio. Instant signal improvement! If you know where the station is broadcasting from, stretch your antenna perpendicular to it — that way, your radio will be able to intercept and pull in more of the signal.

Ham operators eventually set up tall broadcasting and receiving antennas, and need to be cautious of lightning strikes. Lightning can disable your entire house current and phone system, not to mention your radio receivers and senders, so be certain that everything is well-grounded and can be disconnected when a storm passes within five miles.

The Net

Lap-top computers can be battery-operated and are very compatible with an off-the-grid lifestyle. If you've got a telephone and an Internet source in your area, you can be in contact with the world in a way that you can hardly believe. Almost every major library on the planet has a "home page" or listing on the Net, so you have access to services, information, books, loans, and educational videos (for a small additional fee, in some cases) that you might not even know exist. Want to keep up-to-the-minute on earthquakes worldwide? There is a site on the Net. Want to find out the weather predictions for your town, region, state? Want to find out how to prepare Korean Kimchi? Want to know the latest baseball scores, or find out what's happening in a game in progress? How about the severity of that drought in India? Or where UFOs most recently landed? Or what the last English crop circle looks like? It's all there on the Net.

You'll need a computer, which are anything but cheap ($1500-$2000), a telephone, and a membership in an Internet service (about $25 monthly). And it will take you a good six weeks to figure the whole thing out before you feel really comfortable with it.

Most community colleges have courses on using computers, and have free Internet hookups for students... a very inexpensive way to find out if this is a system for you.

Chapter Nine
Generating the Big P
— Power and Batteries

At those times when the electricity goes out for a brief period, your main concern with power and batteries is whether or not your flashlight has got any. But if you are looking at a long stretch without the electric company, alternatives are crucial.

It is possible to generate power at home — in fact, without realizing it, you've been doing some routine things that have created significant amounts of potential electricity which was simply never collected or stored, as we'll see.

I saved this chapter for the end of the book because generating power is a large undertaking. It requires a commitment of time, energy, and often of money, and you will be changed by the decision. You will become very conscious of the use of any powered device, including light bulbs, and conserving power will become a focus of your daily thoughts. All generating systems require maintenance, and it will be very unlikely that you'll find a repair shop nearby that understands the system you use — so you will have to be your own Mr. And Ms. Fix-it. You'll also be nearly immune to the electricity outages that afflict your neighbors.

We'll take a look at various types of systems and their applications, including the extremely low-cost options.

Solar Power

The much-touted "way of the future" really does have numerous benefits for home use: it is very clean, perfectly quiet, has good reliability, and is relatively easily maintained. It is also incredibly expensive compared to the amount of power you can retrieve from the system — and, the way solar-power applications are today, you'll never have cheap power from it. A solar system simply will not sustain an electric cookstove; you'd be wise to use gas-powered refrigerators and freezers to avoid drawing your batteries down to zero.

Here's how it works: the sun shines onto a series of "solar collectors," the flat panels that absorb the light and convert it to tiny pulses of electricity. The number and size of the collectors you use will determine how much power you can obtain from the sun for any given period of time.

Wires in the solar collectors lead away to your battery-storage system, feeding the trickle of electricity into a "controller" and then to an array of "deep discharge" batteries. These are similar to 12-volt car batteries, except that they can withstand repeated charges and discharges better — and, they cost about twice as much as car batteries. The controller limits the amount of power that can enter and leave batteries so they don't become overcharged and ruin the system.

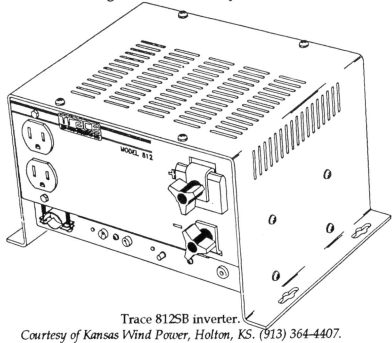

Trace 812SB inverter.
Courtesy of Kansas Wind Power, Holton, KS. (913) 364-4407.

When you wish to use electricity, it travels from the batteries through an "inverter," which changes the electricity from a flow of DC (direct current) to pulses of AC (alternating current), which is what most household appliances and equipment use. (If you have DC lights and appliances, such as can be found on many RVs, you wouldn't need an inverter.) You can use all the energy stored in your batteries (a deep discharge), but if you

44

How To Live Without Electricity
— And Like It

130

want to prolong your battery-life — the time they work before they need to be replaced — you should use only 25% to 50% of the energy stored in them before recharging takes place.

AC Genius inverter.
Courtesy of Kansas Wind Power, Holton, KS. (913) 364-4407.

Energy is replaced in your batteries when the sun shines on your solar panels. It will generally take four hours to two days to fully recharge a system, provided the panels are in full sun.

Let's look at a price list for a small system first:

Two solar panels (used)	$ 400
Solar Controller/Inverter (combination system)	$ 500
Battery (each)	$ 135
Misc. wires and plugs	$ 10
TOTAL	$1045

A battery for this system can store about 400 watt-hours of power. This means, you can run a 100-watt light bulb for four hours before the system is completely drained. You will then need to fully recharge the battery before it can be used again.

Porta Power inverter.
Courtesy of Kansas Wind Power, Holton, KS. (913) 364-4407.

Clearly, you'd immediately look for lower-power alternatives to that 100-watt bulb — and there are plenty. Hardware and department stores carry high-efficiency fluorescents that screw into standard sockets. A 23-watt fluorescent will give light equivalent to a standard 75- to 90-watt incandescent. That 23-watt fluorescent will also set you back about $15 instead of 70¢ for an incandescent bulb.

The high-cost-versus-low-power-returns is the main problem with solar energy generation. In general, over time the solar system costs about three to five times what a typical electric-company hookup would.

Even so, there are ways to save on a solar-power system. Batteries, used but still useable, can be found where rural phone companies are going out of business — oftentimes, they have 2-watt deep discharge batteries by the hundreds which acted as back-up in case their electric hookup went out during storms. When these rural companies close or are taken over by larger companies, they'll often sell older batteries for pennies on the dollar rather than worry about disposing of them at "approved" landfills. Also, you can find used panels at electronics "swap meets" (mostly held on the West Coast), and a few will be offered through catalogs. Don't buy a used inverter unless it comes with a guarantee of replacement or repair if it has problems.

Solar systems can be improved or enlarged by adding panels, batteries, and a larger-capacity inverter. One battery per two panels ought to give plenty of storage power, and ten to twenty batteries can readily power the basic equipment in a house (b/w TV, VCR, lights, small stereo, laptop computer, occasional use of a blender or microwave, fans, etc.). A house-size system can easily run $10,000 to $20,000.

If you are building a house and financing it, you may be able to include part or all or the cost of a solar system in the construction costs — you'll pay for the system over time rather than in a lump sum. Check with your lender or contractor.

Two major dangers facing a solar panel are high winds and hail. Winds can sail panels off into never-never land in the blink of an eye, and hail will disable your system in minutes. If you anticipate hail, make sure you have sturdy canvas tarps on hand that can quickly be thrown over and lashed to your panels — and a few layers of cardboard underneath as padding wouldn't hurt matters any. As for winds: build the sturdiest support system you can afford, and keep a few extra panels on hand, just in case.

Generators, Gas and Diesel

A generator-based electric system is virtually the same as a solar-powered one, with the difference existing in how the power is first created. In a solar system, power comes from the solar panels and sunlight. In the generator system, power comes from the burning of gasoline or diesel, which in turn generates electricity, which is then stored in an array of batteries for later use.

You can also use a generator as backup for a solar system — when the sun doesn't shine sufficiently to charge the system, the generator is pressed into service.

Hooking your generator up to battery storage is the only way to make a generator even remotely cost-efficient. If you try to run your appliances or house lights directly off a generator, you'll spend a fortune to produce very short-term power. Generators lose a good deal of their efficiency through heat, and create a phenomenal amount of carbon monoxide, exhaust, and noise. It would be extremely foolish to use them indoors or in a confined space.

Small Japanese-made generators, designed for camping and short-term use, are relatively quiet, efficient and lightweight. They can power a couple of light bulbs, or a blender or a small TV set — around 300 to 500 watts. They'll run for about five hours on a gallon of gas. In my well-tested opinion, these are the best-made of the lower-cost generators, and require the least repairs.

Sadly, I've found that the lower-cost 1500-to-2000-watt American-made generators no longer have the quality they had a generation ago. If you must get one of these $300-$500 models, plan on replacing it next year and doing a lot of tinkering with it in the interval. They'll run for about one hour at full speed on a gallon of gas, or two hours at half speed. Make certain you get one with a "low-oil shutoff" feature — they drink oil and could easily run out if you don't check every time you fill up. These run at 3600 rpm (revolutions per minute) and wear out their engine comparatively quickly. Gasoline needs to be fresh to run these generators — you can't leave it sitting around for a couple of months, because it undergoes chemical changes that make it difficult to use. Products like "Sta-bil" can help keep gas from changing too much.

Diesel generators, many coming in from China, have a pretty good reputation for reliability and durability. They run at 1800 rpm, so engine wear is reduced compared with gasoline models. During gasoline shortages, diesel fuel may be easier to acquire, since it is vital in the shipping of foods and medical supplies — and diesel doesn't "go bad" as gasoline can, so it can be stored for long periods without problems.

Diesels cost around $1200 for 2500-watt models, and can run as high as $10,000 for high-output systems. I've heard persistent rumors that you can run a diesel with cooking oil if you can't get fuel, but I sure wouldn't want to try that unless I was in dire straits AND had plenty of cooking oil to waste AND wasn't worried about the possibility of wrecking my generator.

Hook your generator up to an electric battery charger ($100) and use this to fully charge your battery collection, just as a solar system does. House power then would be drawn out through the same type of inverter and into appliances.

"Moveable" Battery Power

Your car's 12-volt battery is one of the most useful systems around — it's 100% portable, it is already designed for moderate draws, and it has the capacity to recharge itself every time you turn on the motor. Plus, you already own it if you own the car. With the addition of a small plug-in inverter ($80) that fits into the cigarette lighter, you can run up to a 200-watt device for short periods of time — about 90 minutes. Then, you'll need to start the car, drive around for 15 minutes or so (or just let it idle), and then you can go back to drawing energy from the battery.

We've used the car battery and a small inverter to recharge flashlight batteries when household power was off (you'd need a battery recharger, too, for this type of application). During the 1989 Loma Prieta earthquake in California, we watched pictures of the incident in our living room on a 4-inch TV — power came from the car battery through the cigarette lighter to the small inverter to a regular house electric cord, through a window, and into the TV plug. The draw was so small, about 9 watts, that we didn't even bother to start the car to recharge the battery afterwards.

In the same way, during power outages, you could easily rig up an indoor light hooked to your car battery through the cigarette lighter/inverter system, or even power a few simple appliances as needed.

For a time, whenever we went out for a drive, we'd plug in our rechargeable batteries and make double-use of the car's power. The potential of this simple, relatively inexpensive, and underused system is really quite enormous — you'll think up quite a few applications yourself.

Batteries

The most important feature of batteries — AAAs, AAs, Cs, Ds — is one thing: RECHARGEABILITY.

Many varieties of rechargeables are sold, and most are just as good as any other. If you don't deeply discharge them (run them down to empty), they will literally last for years of constant use. Most standard rechargeables will gradually lose power if they are left sitting on a shelf, so it is fairly standard to leave them in the charger until use. These cost twice the price of alkalines (two Cs for $5, for example), and you will need a charging device that fits your batteries — from $12 to $15, typically.

An improvement over standard rechargeables was made several years ago — alkaline rechargeables, which are sold as "renewal" batteries. These can take up to about 20 charges (more, if you don't deeply discharge them, and always recharge them as soon as possible), and provide a better-quality, longer-lasting power. One real benefit of the renewal types is that they can be charged and then set on a shelf without any power loss for up to five years. In this way, you can have a ready back-up supply without taking up space in the charger.

Renewal batteries are only slightly more expensive than standard rechargeables, but the chargers generally run around $30. If you have a lot of battery-powered devices, renewals will probably give you more satisfaction in the long run, but cost a little more at the start.

We like to keep three sets of batteries for each vital application. For the flashlight, for example, we have two D-size batteries in the light itself, two sitting in the charger, and two on a shelf. In this way, if an emergency takes place, we've got a fully-charged back-up set right there, plus whatever amount of charge was built up in the ones that were recharging, plus whatever remains in the flashlight... perhaps a week's worth of heavily-used potential light. And, we could always hook the charger up to the car battery and recharge any number of Ds as needed (at least until we ran out of gas!). Of course, if we had one of those car-battery solar trickle chargers ($40) that charge your car battery while it sits around, we could probably keep the system going indefinitely.

4 AA solar Nicad battery charger.
Courtesy of Real Goods Trading Corp., Ukiah, CA. (800) 762-7325.

Don't forget that inexpensive solar rechargers can also be found — these run from about $9 (for four AAs) to about $30 (for four AAs or AAAs, and either two Cs or Ds). These charge a good deal more slowly than electric chargers. It might take three to five days to achieve a full charge. This type of charger will be destroyed if it is left out in the rain or if dew enters its tiny solar panel, so it is best to keep them indoors in a sun-facing window.

Improved Solar Super Charger.
Courtesy of Real Goods Trading Corp., Ukiah, CA. (800) 762-7325.

Stand-Alone Systems

Solar charging has also been used to power lights that stand alone — out in a field, as motion detector/security devices, along pathways, and even as electric-fence chargers. They consist of a small solar panel, a storage battery, and the output — either a high efficiency halogen light bulb or electric-fence wire. Security lights also have a motion detector that turns the system on and off, leaving the lights on for only a few minutes at a stretch. All of these will maintain continuous light for only three or four hours, although the security lights generally can go several days on a single charge because they aren't on all the time. Prices run from $35 to $170.

Solar yard lights: Pagoda Solar Light (left) and Dome Yard Light.
Courtesy of Real Goods Trading Corp., Ukiah, CA. (800) 762-7325.

Siemen's Sensor Light
Courtesy of Real Goods Trading Corp., Ukiah, CA. (800) 762-7325.

People and Pet Powers

This is the one part of this book that could be considered truly "experimental," at least for our time in history. The modern treadmill exerciser was once a prison power-supply. Charles Dickens, the creator of Scrooge in *A Christmas Carol*, mentions the evil treadmill in a number of his novels. It was a large device designed to make use of prisoners sentenced to "hard labor." The treadmill was a large, hollow cylinder of wood on an iron frame. Around the circumference were a series of steps about 7½ inches apart. The prisoner, holding handrails, stepped on these, and his weight caused the treadmill to turn, which compelled him to take the next step, and so on. This rotary motion created power which was used in various industries of the time. This "endless stairway" was a type of torture, according to reformers of the day. Wouldn't those good-hearted people be surprised to see today's folks willingly buying and using treadmills at home for "health" reasons!

The treadmill was abolished in 1910, at least for its use by prisoners. However, the physics of the treadmill and its ability to generate power are still as valid as they were then. Surprisingly, many pet animals enjoy running on treadmills or treadmill equivalents — you have only to think of those little wheels in hamster cages, and the larger models that are used by pet rats and squirrels. Dog trainers who have limited space will often have a small treadmill for Fido to run on... the dogs rush to the treadmill as though it were their favorite pastime!

One horse power, circa 1885.

Horses have long been used to run treadmills and water wheels, both standing models and devices that keep the horse walking in a circle on the ground while it pushes a pole. The pole attaches to an upright piece in the center of the circle that turns and transfers rotary energy to an alternator and then to batteries — in effect, the horse's walk becomes a kind of power-generating system. Horses, too, find the easy, predictable movement a way to burn off excess calories and stay in shape during slack seasons.

Plans for these kind of systems exist *somewhere*, but I have not been able to locate them in over ten years of searching. Rumors that Amish families use horse-generated power to run a few electric tools have floated my way for a long time, but I've yet to meet such a family... I'll keep looking.

In the meantime, plans do exist for a simple human-powered generator. Originally, this was published in *The Mother Earth News*, issues 67 and 68 for January/February 1981 and March/April 1981. A wheel-less ten-speed bicycle frame and gear system is used. This is set upon a stand so that the pedals can be comfortably turned by someone sitting on the seat, just like an exercise bike. The rear-wheel gears are attached by pulley to a used Volkswagen flywheel (to stabilize the energy output from the rider's legs), and then the wheel is wired to a used VW alternator. The alternator accepts the rotary motion from the flywheel and converts it to DC current, which flows into a free-standing 12-volt car battery for storage. The outlet wired from the battery is a standard car cigarette-lighter plug outlet. Some welding skill is required to put the system together. With used parts, you'd probably spend less than $100 to set this up.

The human-power can generate about 60 watts of power with continuous medium-speed pedaling (5 amps at 12.5 volts), although a few energetic types could generate about 200 watts for minutes at a stretch. Typically, it would take one minute of pedaling to generate two minutes of useable power. It's not a huge power supply, but if you use an exercise bike anyway, why not store that power and use it to reduce your electric bill?

For the inventor in your home, there are standard-model manual treadmills, along with those stair-stepper devices, that have unused rotary motion going to waste every time they are used. With a little trial and error, that power could be stored, too. (I wouldn't be surprised if self-help magazines were very interested in publishing articles about this kind of device.)

Wrapping It All Up

It is the rare person who will go to the effort to prepare for life without the electric company, whether that might be a temporary or permanent arrangement. After you have taken this direction in life, you won't be fazed by the power outages that harass your neighbors. If there is an earthquake, tornado or other disaster, you'll be there with your flashlight and your wits while other people are groping in the darkness. You will understand why that cheap $30 toaster oven is actually going to cost you hundreds of dollars over its useable life — and you'll be able to make an informed decision about whether it is worth it to you or not. You'll know what to do if power gets to your light bulbs, and you'll know what to do if power can't get there for some reason. You will utterly astonish many of your friends when you mention that you had to start your new refrigerator by lighting a match.

Many people will not understand why you would choose to limit your use of electricity — it's often easiest to simply say, "It cost too much," because people do understand *that*. A few will share your love of independence and self-sufficiency, and will recognize the enjoyment you get from what you are doing.

My only caution for you is the same one I've mentioned many (maybe too many!) times in this book:

don't put all your proverbial eggs into one alternative basket. If you decide to go solar, for example, be certain you also buy a gas or diesel generator for backup. If your spouse HATES the idea of not having access to the power company, then keep the hookup but start weaning your home off the line by using alternate systems such as propane. Your spouse will come around the first time the power goes off during an important TV show, and you can hook the TV up to the car.

Finally, be sensible; know your limitations. Electricity (as they say about "fire") is an excellent servant but a dangerous master. The patience of Job is a big asset when you are trying to figure out wiring or using a wood cookstove for the first time. If you are impulsive or very reactive, let someone else do it for you until they completely understand it — and can explain it to you.

Now, you're ready to live without electricity, and love it!

Resources

Your local library is loaded with self-help and how-to books, plus it probably has back issues of many of these magazines, either on microfilm or in a musty stack somewhere — ask the librarian. They love to help.

Magazines and Catalogs

Back Home Magazine, PO Box 370, Mountain Home, NC 28758. Organic and ecological orientation.

Backwoods Home Magazine, 1257 Siskiyou Blvd., #213, Ashland, OR 97520. Practical and conservative.

Countryside and Small Stock Journal, W11564 Hwy. 64, Withee, WI 54498. Reader-written and often has very interesting tidbits on small engines and other systems.

Home Power Magazine, PO Box 520, Ashland, OR 97520. 1-800-707-6585. Devoted to solar, wind and hydro power systems, *Home Power* is 114 pages of "how-to" and "how-we-did-it" type articles, along with plenty of ads for photovoltaics, batteries, wind turbines, pumps, inverters, solar trackers, and books.

Kansas Wind Power Catalog, 13569 214th Rd., Holton, KS 66436. 1-913-364-4407. Catalog is $4. Many non-electric applications besides windmills (which they also have). Solar cookers, inverters, grain mills, water pumps, propane, books, shortwave radios, foods, and books. Good prices, too.

Lehman's Non-Electrical Catalog, $2. PO Box 41, Kidron, OH 44636, 1-330-857-5757. This is the place the Amish go to shop, so you know the stuff must be pretty good quality. Fast mail service and helpful staff.

The Mother Earth News. Old issues number 1 through about 80. This is the original self-help magazine (heavy on tofu recipes, living in sod huts, and other unusual alternatives), and loaded with really useful projects in almost every issue. After issue 80, the info became more backyard project oriented.

Real Goods Catalog, 555 Leslie St., Ukiah, CA 95482-5576. 1-800-762-7325. Solar applications, both big and small, plus a bunch of other stuff. Offers annual "solar tours" of houses and buildings which use solar energy in various ways. Also offers books on *Straw Bale Construction* and a *Solar Living Sources Book.*

Small Farmer's Journal, PO Box 1627, Sisters, OR 97402. This is aimed toward people who use draft horses, but contains many handy designs and plans for old-style farm implements and systems.

Books

The Bread Book, A Natural Whole-Grain Seed-to-Loaf Approach to Real Bread, by Thom Leonard. Published by East-West Health Books, 17 Station St., Brookline, MA 02146, 1990, $8.95. Recipes, grain-growing suggestions, small but chock-full of neat stuff. This is the book that has plans for an outdoor brick bread oven — it's portable if you have a front-end loader.

Cooking With the Sun, How to Build and Use Solar Cookers, by Beth Halacy and Dan Halacy, Morning Sun Press, 1240 Quandt Road, Lafayette, CA 94549, 1992, 114 pages, $7.95. Excellent reference on solar application to ovens and "stoves" heated by the sun — probably the one with clearest directions and ease of use. Recipes, too.

Electronic Troubleshooting and Repair Handbook, by Homer L. Davison, McGraw Hill, 1995, 1071 pages, hardcover, $60. Extensive and detailed information on electronic systems of all kinds — a big help if you plan to set up an at-home electric generation system.

Foxfire Books, Anchor, Doubleday Press. This collection from the 1970s represents the efforts of young people to save the knowledge of their forebears — and the entire series is just loaded with fascinating pictures, directions, ideas and applications for hands-on do-it-yourselfers. Warning: once you start reading these, you can't stop.

Living On Less, published by Mother Earth News, 1984. 225 pages, softcover. If you can find one of these gems, grab it. Includes low-tech applications on housing, foraging, canning, livestock, housewares, health, recreation, and of course, ways to cut your energy costs.

Living Without Electricity, by Steven Scott and Kenneth Pellman. Published by Good Books, 3510 Old Philadelphia Pike, Intercourse, PA 17534. Softcover, 1990, 125 pages, $5.95. Aside from an interesting peek into Amish lifestyles, this book also has some excellent adaptable non-electric systems with photos. Best of all, it has a super bibliography that refers to even more books and magazines about historical applications and systems (such as windmills and alternative lighting).

Practical Skills, A Revival of Forgotten Crafts, Techniques and Traditions, by Gene Logsdon. Published by Rodale Press, Emmaus, Pa, 1985. Extensive store of information on many, many non-electrical applications. Excellent section on cisterns and pond construction. If there is a better book on general subjects related to self-sufficiency, I've never seen it.

Solar Science Projects, by D.S. Halacy, Jr. Published by Scholastic Book Service, 1971. For young people, but loaded with applications including a "solar forge" for melting metal, and a crystal radio powered by the sun.

Books on the Edge

These may not have immediate application to a non-electric lifestyle, but they do have some interesting projects for do-it-yourselfers who also like electric self-sufficiency.

Building Your Own Laser, Phaser, Ion Ray Gun and Other Working Space-Age Projects, by Robert E. Iannini. Published by Tab Books, 1983. 390 pages, softcover, $21.95. If you are a tinkerer and want to make something nobody else in the neighborhood has (or has even thought of) try these babies.

Cross Currents, The Perils of Electropollution, the Promise of Electromedicine, by Robert O. Becker, MD. Published by Jeremy P. Tarcher, Los Angeles, 1990. 336 pages, softcover. $12.95. Dr. Becker was probably the premiere pioneer researcher in the field of electricity as a possible medical tool — and he has stern warnings about the "electropollution" in our environment.

If there is one book that will convince you to go off-the-grid, this is it.

Mind Machines You Can Build, by G. Harry Stine. Published by Top of the Mountain Press, Largo, FL 34643-5117. 1992, 208 pages, softcover, $11.95. Diagrams, ideas, and the fringe of our understanding of various types of energies — but easy to read and interesting.

How to Build Earthquake, Weather and Solar Flare Monitors, by Gary G. Giusti. Published by McGraw Hill, 1995. 290 pages, softcover, $19.95. A real guidebook for making some free-standing monitors that really work. The appendices are extensive and cover useful information of the laws of electricity, parts suppliers, and the meaning of electrical schematic symbols (which a number of other authors seem to take for granted that you understand). Plus, you can detect local teeny earthquakes!

Index